The Musical Clock

The Musical Clock

Claude B. Reeve

MODEL & ALLIED PUBLICATIONS
ARGUS BOOKS LIMITED
Station Road, Kings Langley
Herts, England.

Model & Allied Publications
Argus Books Limited
Station Road, Kings Langley,
Herts, England.

First Published 1975
© Claude B. Reeve 1975
ISBN 0 85242 423 X

Set in IBM Press Roman by
Type Practitioners Ltd, Sevenoaks
Printed by
Clarke, Doble & Brendon Ltd, Plymouth

Foreword

At some time or other in their career most model engineers are tempted to try their hands at clockmaking either to placate a spouse tired of sweeping up swarf, to justify to that same spouse the expense of new workshop equipment, or simply that the fascination of making a wide variety of small parts to assemble into a working clock has gripped them. There is indeed a subtle charm about everything to do with clocks both old and new and once launched into their manufacture many a tyro finds himself so intrigued with the variety of work involved that he cannot rest until he has achieved expert status.

Claude B. Reeve is undoubtedly the man to generate and foster this enthusiasm. Looking back over the years to the thirties and earlier we find records of his work, either creating new designs, renovating old and valuable mechanisms, or what he likes doing best, producing classic, ageless designs that we believe well qualified to stand besides some of the great clockmakers of the past. He has regularly published drawings and descriptions of his work, attends exhibitions where clocks are on display, and enjoyed meeting people who make clocks, has a wide correspondence circle throughout the world, and in this way is particularly well qualified not only to make exquisite pieces of machinery, but to impart his knowledge in a readily understandable fashion.

It would be idle to suggest that his Musical Clock is easy to make but it should be within the capabilities of the average model engineer who owns a 2½in lathe or larger and the associated workshop equipment. The description is confined to the actual work on the clock including the chiming mechanism.

In going ahead the enthusiast will find many delightful opportunities of breaking off work to embark on essential sidelines. There are numerous simple but desirable additional tools that can be made to facilitate work. Such forays enliven the working evenings and who better than the ever inventive model engineer to savour the joys of making tools to make tools . . .

It is indeed a superb chiming and striking clock and we would wish pride and joy to all who build it . . . and lasting pleasure over the years as it occupies a place of honour in hall or lounge.

Contents

Musical side of movement

CHAPTER ONE

Introduction, the pendulum and the plates

This book gives detailed instructions for making one of the most advanced clocks in the world. The construction is well within the capabilities of the average model engineer provided he has a small lathe–say, one with a 2 1/2 in. or 3 in. centre height, a small drilling machine and the ability to work fairly well in metal.

The movement is rather complicated but all its actions can be comfortably viewed when in operation. Construction is described step by step with alternative methods of approach for carrying out some of the details.

Details of the pendulum

Fig. 1 shows the completed pendulum which is drawn to scale. A start can be made on the pendulum rod (Item 1). This is made either of mild steel or invar steel (non-expandable steel) of 5/16 in. dia. Invar steel rod will make a very accurate pendulum having no temperature error. The extreme accuracy of the invar pendulum will, however, be lost to some extent in this type of movement due to the unlocking of the chiming train, which must have a very slight effect on the rate of the time train.

Cut the rod to a length of 3 ft. 7 1/4 in., thread the upper end of the rod for about 1/4 in. with a 5/16 in. x 40 thread die. Follow the same procedure for the lower end of the rod, except in this case the threaded part should extend to approximately 1 1/2 in. from the end of the rod. This operation is better carried out in the lathe; the rod should be passed through the mandrel and clamped in the self-centring chuck.

Steadying the rod

The free end of the rod, beyond the tail end of the mandrel, should be steadied with a hole in a piece of wood or tied up with string to prevent it whipping about. The extreme ends of the rod should be slightly tapered before using the die. This can be done while running in the lathe, either with a file or graver.

If using invar steel rod, take care to close the die very gradually and always open the die before passing back over the thread again. Passing back causes the thread to strip.

While still in the lathe, the end of the rod should be drilled 3/32 in. and tapped 1/8 in. Whitworth to accommodate the pointer (Item No. 2). Item No. 3 represents the rating nut. It is shown in Fig. 1 and Fig. 2. It should be made from phosphor bronze or hard brass to the dimensions shown.

. Chuck a length of metal in the self-centring chuck with, say, 3/4 in. protruding from the jaws. Face the end square and centre drill it with a slocombe drill. Next take a fine cut on the rod to brighten it; the free end should now be steadied with

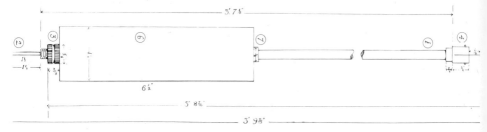

Fig. 1   The pendulum

the tailstock centre and the rod then knurled for a length of about 1/2 in. Afterwards it should be drilled and bored to a diameter of 9/32 in. and then threaded with a 5/16 in. x 40 thread tap. The half-round groove situated midway in the length of the nut can now be turned with a hand tool, or with a form tool in the slide-rest. Finally it should be parted off to a length of 3/8 in.

Fitting the nut and rod

It is wise to make the nut first, before threading the rod, as it is most important that the fit should be really good, not too tight but without shake.

The next item to make is No. 4 (Fig. 1) and Nos. 4 and 4A (Fig. 2). This is the brass suspension block which is screwed on to the upper end of the rod. It is made from a piece of hard drawn 1/2 in. square brass rod. A short length of the rod should be chucked in the four-jaw chuck leaving a length of 3/4 in. projecting from the jaws.

Drill, bore and tap to a length of 1/4 in. and thread the hole 40 tpi. It will be necessary to use a second or plug tap for finishing the threading of this hole. Next turn down the end of the rod to a diameter of 7/16 in. x 1/4 in. length. The rod should now be cut to a length of 13/16 in. with a fine hacksaw. Reverse in chuck and face the end off square.

The block has now to be cut down the centre with a fine circular saw of 8 thou. thickness to a length of 5/16 in. If no saw is available, it can be accomplished by filing out a wide slot, say, 3/16 in. wide, then filing two pieces of brass to fill the slot, making allowance for the thickness of the suspension spring, which should be 8 thou. in thickness.

Finishing the block

Fit the two pieces of brass in the slot with a spare piece of suspension spring in the centre. Now flux and soft-solder the joints, being careful to keep the flux and solder away from the spring in the centre. Soldering is best carried out by holding the work piece over the bunsen burner. When cool, pull out the spring and thoroughly wash the block with soap and water. This is most important.

The block can now be filed up and finished, not forgetting to drill a 3/32 in. hole at a distance of 3/16 in. from the top end of the block. Next, a steel pin should be turned up and finished to be a nice push-in fit in the hole. To make the hole in the spring, first make a punch to fit the hole in the block; the face of the punch should be made dead flat and at right angles to the sides of the punch. It can be hardened but this is not absolutely necessary.

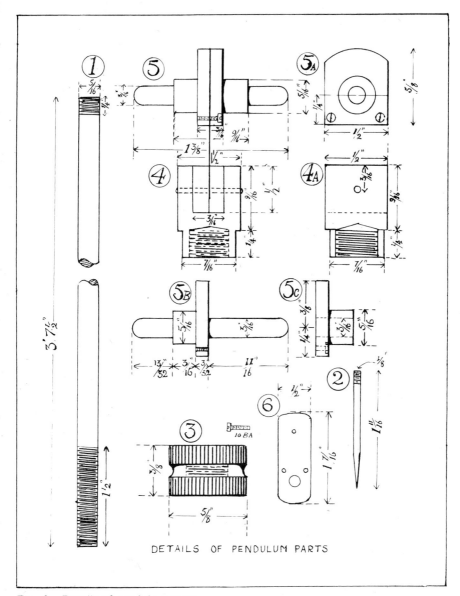

Fig. 2 Details of pendulum parts

Now position the spring in the slot of the block, taking care to keep the spring quite central. Place on vice or anvil, give punch one blow with the hammer, and a perfect circular hole in the spring will be formed, without any distortion having taken place.

Attention must now be given to the trunnion to which the upper end of the suspension spring is attached. This is shown in Fig. 1 (No. 5) and in Fig. 2 (Nos. 5 and 5A) and is also shown exploded in 5B and 5C. Chuck a piece of 3/4 in. dia. mild steel rod in the self-centring chuck, leaving a 3/4 in. length protruding from

3

the chuck jaws. Centre with a slocombe drill, support the end with a tailstock centre, turn down to a length of 11/16 in. and to a diameter of 3/16 in. smoothing it off with emery sticks, not forgetting to round off the end as shown.

It is also as well slightly to recess the inside wall of the flange about its centre. Reverse in the chuck, centre-drill the end and support it with the tailstock centre. Now make a mark at a distance of 3/32 in. measured from the inner edge of the wall of the flange just previously formed. Next turn down to a diameter of 5/16 in. to meet the mark made on the flange and then file another mark at a distance of 3/16 in., measured from the outer side of the flange.

Now turn down the remainder of the rod to a diameter of 3/16 in., the length of this spigot when finished to be approximately 13/32 in., and finally round the end. Make the sliding flange from a short length of 3/4 in. dia. mild steel rod. It is better to start with a stiff fit to the other part of the trunnion, so that the holes for the screws and suspension spring can be drilled through both flanges at the same time. A No. 55 drill is a suitable tapping size for the two 10 B.A. countersunk screws.

A simple jig

After the screws have been fitted, the flanges should be filed up and finished to the shape shown in the drawing, taking particular care to keep the bottom edges square with the sides and it is usual to make a very slight bevel to the bottom inside edges of the flanges that butt against the suspension spring. The suspension spring should now have the three other holes made to fit the holes in the trunnion and these holes in the spring should be easy-fitting. Punch the holes as described before, but in this case a jig should be made, which is merely a strip of 1/32 in. thick brass, bent double, with the holes drilled through both thicknesses. Insert the suspension spring in the jig with the position marked where the hole is required, and punch through as before.

In Fig. 2 (No. 6) the suspension spring is shown upside down. Try the spring in the trunnion, and see that it hangs quite perpendicular. The complete trunnion should be fine finished all over with emery and buff sticks.

Attention should now be given to the pendulum bob. This can be described as a brass cylinder filled with lead. This is shown in Fig. 1 (No. 6) and again in Fig. 3 (Nos. 1 and 2). The drawings are self-explanatory and it will be observed that the brass casing or jacket and the lead casting are separate entities. The brass jacket is a sliding fit over the lead casting.

It is better to make the jacket first. Procure a length of brass tube 6 1/2 in. long x 1 3/4 in. dia. and 1/16 in. thick. True the ends of the tube in the lathe, if possible with the aid of the three-point steady and self-centring chuck. In the absence of a steady, the ends of the tube can be trued by gripping the outside walls of the tube with the chuck jaws and supporting the other end of the tube with a disc of brass temporarily soft-soldered a short distance within the end of the tube.

The disc first having a small hole drilled centrally through it, the pointed tailstock centre will support it quite safely while the ends are being trued up.

Now turn a 3/32 in. thick brass disc to the same diameter as that of the outside wall of the tube, followed by turning away half the thickness of the disc so that the spigot thus formed will be a tight fit in the end of the tube. The disc should be

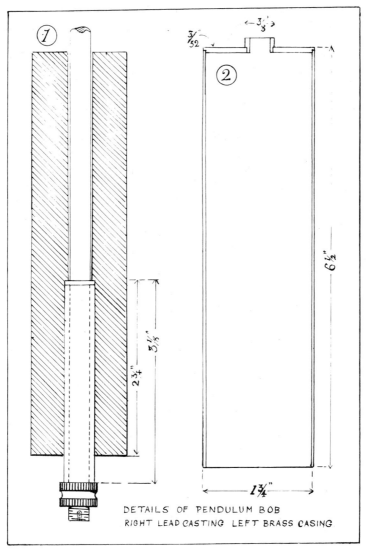

DETAILS OF PENDULUM BOB
RIGHT LEAD CASTING LEFT BRASS CASING

Fig. 3   Details of pendulum bob. Right lead casting, left brass casing

soft-soldered to the end of the tube. Do the soldering over a bunsen burner—a soldering iron is not suitable for this operation.

Fig. 1 (No. 7) shows a small flanged bush of brass which should next be made. It should be a drive-in fit to a central hole in the disc, but its hole should be a sliding fit to the pendulum rod.

Casting the lead

The lead bob can now be cast. Obtain a small wooden box or tin and half fill it with dry sand or loam. Position the brass tube with the top end well buried in the sand, taking care that the tube is really vertical. Now take a short length of 5/16 in.

5

dia. steel rod slightly longer than the tube, roll half a dozen turns of cartridge paper round the rod and stick the paper to prevent it unwinding. The paper should extend from the bottom of the tube to, say, 1/2 in. from the top of the tube.

Find a tin lid (a boot polish tin does very well); drill a central hole 5/16 in. in diameter and also cut a very large hole towards the side of the tin lid, but avoid getting it too near either the central hole or the outer edge of this disc. Next place the steel rod in the tube, inserting the end of the rod through the bush into the sand. Position the tin disc in the tube so that it is just below the top edge of the tube with the upper end of the steel rod passing through the central hole (previously made) in the tin disc.

To make sure that the tube will not stick to the lead when it is poured, it is as well to line the tube with, say, three thicknesses of cartridge paper. The lead can now be melted and poured. In the absence of a proper ladle, an aluminium saucepan makes an excellent substitute.

The lead should be poured in one go and enough provided to come just below the level of the tin disc. After the lead has cooled it will be found that the paper has done its job satisfactorily in preventing the lead sticking to either the tube or the steel rod. The burnt paper should be removed and it will be found that the brass tube and the pendulum rod are both a nice easy fit to the lead casting.

If invar steel is used for the pendulum rod, the lead bob should have the hole enlarged by boring from the bottom end to a distance approximately 2 3/4 in. and a steel washer inserted for the end of a piece of steel tube to butt against as shown in Fig. 3. The other end of the steel tube will rest on the rating nut.

Assembling the pendulum

If, however, a mild steel rod is used for the pendulum rod it will be better to leave the bob as it is and place a large steel washer between the top of the rating nut and the bottom end of the bob.

The completed pendulum can now be assembled, but the final polishing of the casing of the bob should be left till later.

Making the frame

As will be seen from Fig. 4 the frame consists of a back plate 8 in. wide x 7 in. high x 1/8 in. thickness. There are three front plates. The dimensions of the centre plate are 7 in. high x 2 in. wide, and the left-hand and right-hand plates each measure respectively 7 in. high x 2 7/8 in. wide. It will be noted that the frame is held together by 12 pillars, four to each section.

The brass plate for the frame can be obtained from Messrs John Smith and Sons, St. John's Square, Clerkenwell, London, E. The firm will supply metal known as soft compo. engraving brass which is specially suitable for clock plates. It chips well when being drilled and is very suitable for drilling very small holes—it is, however, not always supplied in a flat condition and may need planishing. There is another kind of brass the firm will supply; this is very truly flat and rather hard. I have found it quite suitable for clockmaking provided care is taken with the drilling operations and as there are no very small holes to be drilled in the construction of this movement it will be quite suitable for the purpose in hand.

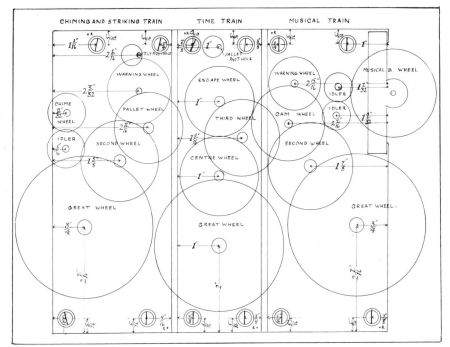

Fig. 4 General arrangement of wheels between the plates

Drilling the plates

To make the frame, roughly true up the edges of the back plate and do the same with the three front plates. Now position the three front plates on top of the back plate and tack the edges of the plates together here and there with soft solder.

Looking at Fig. 4, it will be seen there are two black dots marked on each front plate; these dots indicate the position where holes are to be drilled, say, 1/16 in. or slightly less in diameter. The drilling can be done through both plates at once, or, if preferred, through the front plate and partly through the back plate, and the drilling of the latter completed after the plates have been separated.

Remove the solder from the edges of the plates and separate them. Broach the holes in the three front plates using a taper broach and broach the holes from the front surface of the plates. Six small taper steel pins are now made and firmly driven into the previously made tapered holes in the three front plates. The pins should protrude 1/8 in. from the underside of the plate. Now finish drilling the holes in the backplate followed by broaching them out to suit the taper pins.

It is important that this part of the work should be well done as all future operations on the plates will depend on these positioning pins.

The edges of the plates can be finally trued up. A good way to do this is to put a long flat file in the bench vice and then rub the edges of the plates on the file followed by various grades of emery sticks also held in the jaws of the bench vice in place of the file.

Be sure to remove every trace of burrs from all the edges of the plates. Do no more to the plates until the pillars have been made which will next be described.

7

CHAPTER TWO

The pillars and wheel cutting

The pillars, wheel cutting and the three driving barrels are among the items discussed in this chapter.

The pillars are made from a length of hard-drawn brass rod of 1/2 in. dia. (Fig. 5). Begin by cutting each pillar to a length of, say, 2 11/16 in., chuck each in turn in the self-centring chuck and face both ends off true and square and, at the same time, centre-drill both ends with the slocombe drill.

Now turn a spigot at each end of the rod 3/16 in. in diameter to leave the unturned rod to measure 2 5/16 in. in length as shown in the drawing. One spigot of each pillar has to be threaded with a 3/16 in. x 40 thread die (or any other size fine thread will do). To get the thread right up to the shoulder, reverse the die in the die holder. Before finishing off these threads it is as well to drill and tap a suitable size hole in a spare piece of plate and test the fit of the threaded spigots of the pillars.

Now reverse the pillars in the chuck and drill a short hole 3/32 in. dia. and thread up with a 1/8 in. Whitworth tap. The pillars can be turned to the shape shown in the drawing. Ten pillars will be required as No. 1, and two pillars as No. 2 (Fig. 5).

Lathe set up for wheel-cutting

These two pillars have a broader central boss for the reception of the set screws that hold the movement to the wooden seat board. They should be drilled and tapped 3 B.A. but this drilling and tapping should be left until the pillars have been finally fitted to the back plate to ensure that the tapped holes are quite vertical when the pillars are tightened up.

To ensure a good finish on the pillars, they should be planished with a hand tool and I have found that an ordinary carpenter's wood chisel is excellent for the purpose, provided it is well whetted on an oil stone. The small radius shown on the edges of the bosses can be produced by a hand form tool made from a bradawl. Finally each pillar should be finished off with fine emery sticks.

The 12 steel screws and brass washers for holding the three front plates to the pillars should next be made. The screws should be made from a short length of 3/8 in. mild steel round rod; a spigot of 1/8 in. dia. and 1/4 in. length should be turned. After cutting the thread, the end of the screw should be rounded off followed by polishing with an emery stick. This applies to all the screws used in the construction of the clock.

Next part off each screw in the lathe. If you are not very successful in using the parting tool, cut them through with a miniature hacksaw with the mandrel turning slowly. Next grip gently each screw by the threaded portion with the jaws of the chuck and the underside of the screw head butting against the face of the chuck jaws.

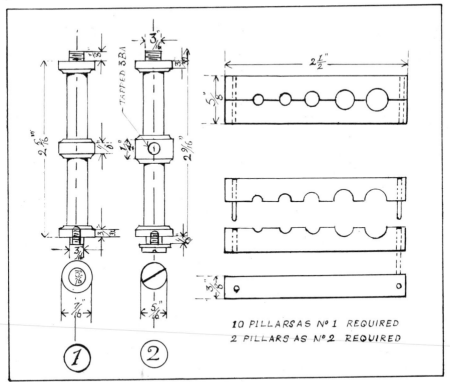

Fig. 5   The pillars and a jig for holding the screws

Now, with a sharp round-nose tool, face off the head of the screw smoothly. The screw should be transferred to the vice and the slot cut with a fine hacksaw. Take out the turning marks by holding the head of the screw well down a No. 2 emery stick held in the vice. Continue with finer emery sticks and for a final finish a No. 000 will produce a mirror-like finish.

The brass washers are turned from a length of brass rod held in the self-centring chuck and require holding in the fingers and smoothing and finishing off the same way as the screws.

The plates can be drilled to receive the pillars at the positions shown in the drawings. Commence the drilling by using a 1/16 in. drill. Drill all the holes in the front plate first and remove all burrs. Now assemble the front and back plates together and, using the holes previously drilled in the front plate as a guide, drill the holes in the back plate. Only the minimum amount of drilling should be done—just sufficient to mark the position for the pillar. Remove the front plates and finish the drilling.

The reason for not drilling through both plates at once is that the swarf collects between the plates, causing them to lift and bring them out of correct register with one another. This rule applies to all drilling operations in regard to the plates.

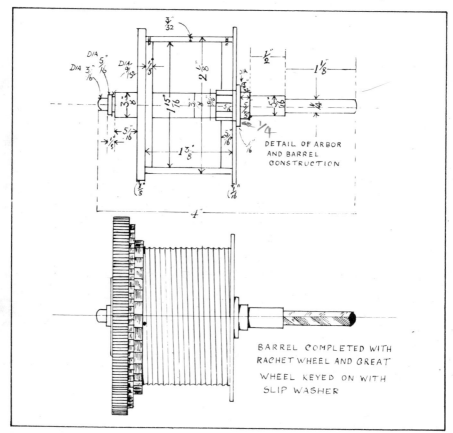

Fig. 6 Driving barrel and arbor

All the holes in the front plates should be enlarged to 3/16 in. dia.; the holes in the back plate, however, should be finally drilled with a No. 21 gauge drill and tapped with a 3/16 in. x 40 thread tap, afterwards slightly countersinking the holes so that the pillars screw home flush with the plate. The spigots of the pillars that fit the holes in the front plates should be of such a length as to be just below the level of the height of the washers. Then, when the screws are inserted, the plates will tighten up perfectly.

The complete frame can now be assembled, but it is as well to make each pillar to its respective position on the plates. A glance at Fig. 4 will show that certain sections of the plates have been cut away. Do nothing about this at the moment.

Figs. 6 and 7 show the construction of the three driving barrels. These are all of the same dimensions so far as the drum portion is concerned. There is a slight difference in the pivoted portion of their arbors which can be disregarded for the present.

Begin by cutting to a length of 4 1/4 in., a piece of 5/8 in. dia. silver steel, chuck and turn each end to a 60 deg. cone. File a fine nick at about 1 31/32 in. from one end to serve as a datum line which should be further marked by turning a groove on the rod in the lathe with a fine knife tool. The remainder of the rod, approximately 2 9/32 in., should now be turned down to, say, a diameter of a full 1/2 in.

At a distance of 3/8 in., taken from the shoulder just formed, make another nick; the remainder of the rod from this nick should now be turned down to a diameter somewhat over 3/8 in. Next the 1/2 in. portion is filed eight-sided, taking care to avoid filing into the 5/8 in. shoulder. Then take a 2 1/2 in. x 1/4 in. thick circular brass blank and centrally drill a hole of such a size that it can be filed eight-sided to be a drive-on fit on the arbor.

To drive the circular blank onto the arbor, grip the arbor in the bench vice by the upturned portion of the rod. Place the circular blank in position and drive home with a hammer and a hollow punch improvised from a tube spanner. Place in lathe between the centres and test for truth. It may be a little out, but this can be disregarded as it will require turning anyway.

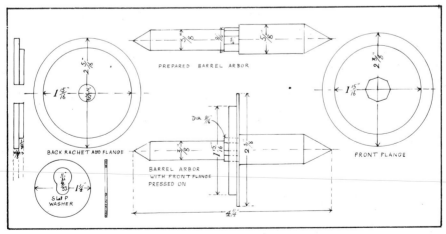

Fig. 7 Parts of barrel assembly

Before mounting the circular blank it is prudent to turn a minute recess between the eight-sided portion and 5/8 in. dia. shoulder. This will ensure the blank going right home and making an invisible join with the shoulder on the arbor. Next cut a 4 1/2 in. length of brass tube into three equal lengths. The outside diameter of the tube should be 2 1/8 in. and the thickness of the walls of the tube should be 3/32 in.

Chuck each length in turn in the self-centring chuck and true both ends of the tube so that the length is 1 3/8 in., taking particular care to remove all burrs. Now, with the arbor mounted between the hollow centres in the lathe, turn the seating for the brass tube which should be a tight fit on the step just turned. The step should be 3/16 in. wide. This will leave about 1/16 in. thickness for the flange.

Now skim down the 3/8 in. dia. portion of the arbor and leave it with a smooth finish. Prepare another 1/4 in. thick x 2 1/2 in. dia. brass blank to form the other face to the barrel. The hole in the blank should be bored a good fit to the 3/8 in. dia. of the barrel arbor. If the blank is chucked in the self-centring chuck with the lathe jaws in position, so arranged that slightly more than half the thickness of the blank protrudes from the chuck jaws, it will be found that the boring of the hole and the turning of the step can be done at the same setting; approximately half the thickness of the blank is turned away in this case to form the step which is also made a close fit to the tube. With all three parts of the winding drum or barrel prepared it should now be assembled.

See that all is well pressed firmly home. Drill three small holes, say, No. 55 gauge drill size, equidistant from each other near both ends of the tube into the thickness of the steps formed on the circular blanks. Tap each hole with a 10 B.A. tap and screw in short lengths of prepared 10 B.A. brass rod quite tightly and cut off flush with the outside wall of the tube. The barrel should be returned to the lathe and turned true all over; for the time being do nothing further with either end of its arbor.

The question now arises as to the screwcutting of the barrel for the groove to guide the driving line. It will make no difference to the going of the clock whether the groove is cut or not, provided the movement is mounted level in its going position, neither leaning backwards or forwards. If it is decided to screwcut the barrel, set the screwcutting gear to give 12 threads per inch and the cutting tool should have a half round-nosed tip and be slightly over 1/16 in. in width.

The other two barrels should be made to the same dimensions stated, but the final finishing of all three had better be left until the wheels have been cut, which will next be described.

Some readers may wish to purchase their sets of wheels with the teeth already cut. They can be obtained from Christopher Rycroft, Scarr House, Stainland, Nr. Halifax, Tel: Elland 4255.

To do the wheelcutting oneself is not very difficult provided there are suitable means of dividing for the numbers of the teeth required.

Fig. 8 (No. 1) shows a simple piece of apparatus that will do the cutting part of the job very well. It should be mounted on the slide rest in place of the tool post and the pulley on the cutter arbor should be belted to a small fractional electric motor, mounted in a vertical position and screwed to a hinged board fixed on the wall at the back of the lathe, so arranged that by swinging the hinged board backwards or forwards an even tension of the belt is maintained between pulley on the electric motor and the pulley on the cutter frame arbor as different diameters of the wheels are being cut. The drawing is self-explanatory, as to how the cutter frame is constructed.

The cone bearings

It is difficult to give dimensions as this to some extent depends on the centre height of the lathe on which it is to be used. My lathe has a centre height of 2 3/4 in., so I made my frame about 4 in. high and built the frame from 1/2 in. square mild steel rod. As will be seen in the drawing the frame is held together with 1/4 in. dia. bolts. The cone bearings were also made from 1/4 in. dia. bolts and there is provision for height adjustment. This is important and will be explained later.

The cutter arbor was made from a short length of round steel rod; a portion of the rod was turned down to 1/4 in. dia. to fit the hole in the clock wheel cutter. The cone bearings are better for being case-hardened and should be run in a little before being put to definite use.

Referring to Fig. 8 again, the three fitments, Nos. 2, 3 and 4, are for holding blank wheels that require turning and having the teeth cut. No. 2 should have its spigot turned to a diameter of 3/16 in. and threaded to take a nut. No. 3 has a spigot of 3/8 in. dia. and will also need threading and a nut fitted. No. 4 is a fitment from which it will be seen that a wood disc is secured to its face plate by two or

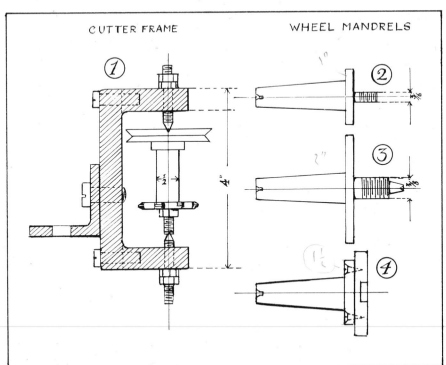

Fig. 8 Attachments for wheel cutting

three wood screws put in from the back. The face of the wood disc is turned true and its diameter turned down a little less than the diameter of the blank wheel. The blank wheel is next centre popped and two small holes are drilled through the blank at any convenient position.

Now hold the blank against the wood disc, bring up the tailstock and hold the blank in position by entering the point of the tailstock centre into the centre-popped sink in the blank. While held thus, two small screws are put through the blank into the wood disc. The blank can be turned to size and have its centre hole bored true to the run of the wheel. At the same setting the teeth of the wheel can be cut.

A suggested way to make a division plate is to mount a disc of wood on the tail end of the mandrel. Turn it to a diameter of 22 1/2 in. and around its periphery fasten an ordinary 5 ft. tape measure. Arrange a stiff spring and pointer that can register each 1/8 in. division—this will give 360 divisions and multiples of this number.

Drilling through the disc

Now mount a brass disc on the lathe faceplate and a drilling spindle on the slide rest. Drill each hole through the brass disc with a 1/16 in. drill. It is as well to have only a very small amount of drill protruding from the chuck. To obtain other divisions the tape measure can be cut and the wooden disc turned down to suit the reduced length of the tape measure.

The time train wheels consist of the great wheel, 120 teeth x 40 dp, the full diameter of blank being 3 in.; the centre wheel 1/16 in. thick, 96 teeth x 52 dp, the full diameter being 2 in.; the third wheel 1/16 in. thick, 90 teeth x 52 dp, the full diameter being 1 13/16 in.; the escape-wheel (dead beat) 30 teeth, full diameter 1 13/16 in.

Circular milling cutters can be obtained from Mr. Phillip Thornton, Great Haywood, Staffs., the cutters that Mr. Thornton supplies are on the module system, but have been matched to the DP system as used in the construction of this clock, the following cutters will be required.

Time Train	Musical Train
DP 40 = .65/W (wheel)	DP 34 = .75/W (wheel)
DP 40 = .55/10 (pinion)	DP 34 = .65/8 (pinion)
DP 52 = .5/W (wheel)	DP 40 = .65/W (wheel)
DP 52 = .45/12 (pinion)	DP 40 = .55/8 (pinion)

Strike Train	Motion
DP 34 = .75/W (wheel)	DP 44 = .575/W (wheel)
DP 34 = .65/10 (pinion)	DP 44 = .5/8 (pinion)
DP 42 = .6/W (wheel)	
DP 42 = .55/8 (pinion)	
DP 48 = .525/W (wheel)	
DP 48 = .45/* (pinion)	
DP 52 = .5/W (wheel)	
DP 52 = .45/8 (pinion)	

This range will cut all the wheels contained in the movement.

A brass circular blank 3 1/8 in. dia. x 1/4 in. thick will be required for the great wheel; this should be chucked in the self centring or four jaw chuck and have both faces skimmed true. It will be found that very little machining will be necessary to obtain this. Next machine out the recess or sink, of which the outer wall is 2 1/2 in. dia. and the inner wall a full 9/16 in. dia. The depth of the sink should be 3/32 in.

Drilling the centre hole

Next, drill and bore the centre hole carefully to 3/8 in. dia. It must be made a good fit to the 3/8 in. spigot of the wheel mandrel chuck (Fig. 8, No. 3) and the latter fitted to the lathe mandrel very firmly. Now place the circular blank on the wheel mandrel with the sink side facing outwards (not forgetting to put a washer between the nut and the blank wheel).

Fit the cutter to the cutter arbor so that the cutting edges of its teeth will revolve anti-clockwise and see that the cutter is adjusted to cut dead on centre with the lathe centres—otherwise staggered teeth will be the result. Assuming that the division plate is fixed on the tail end of the mandrel and that the spring pointer is also fixed with its point in a hole of the 120 hole circle, the cross-slide should now be adjusted to cut approximately three-quarters of the depth of space between two teeth and locked in this position. All other slides that are not being used should also be locked.

Either by using the top slide feed-screw or the leadscrew, take the first cut through the blank wheel. With a thick wheel it is necessary to stop the rotation of the cutter before backing out in readiness for the next cut. For thinner blank wheels of, say, 1/16 in. thickness this is unnecessary if the cutter is withdrawn quickly with the aid of the lathe rack hand wheel.

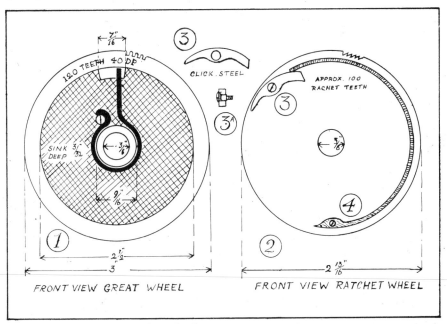

Fig. 9   The great and ratchet wheel

Having gone round the wheel once, the final cut can now be done. The cross-slide should be unlocked and carefully advanced and a trial cut taken on two adjacent tooth spaces. To ensure a well formed tooth, it is better to leave a minute flat on the top of the tooth rather than advance the cutter too close to the wheel. Should this occur, it seems to produce a lopsided-looking tooth and, of course, the wheel will be undersized.

The next wheel to be cut is the large maintaining ratchet wheel which is approximately 2 13/16 in. dia. x 3/32 in. thickness. This ratchet wheel and the great wheel are seen in Fig. 9 (Nos. 1 and 2) and again in Fig. 10 (Nos. 1 and 2). The blank ratchet wheel should be chucked on the same wheel mandrel as was used for the great wheel. It required no sinks on either of its faces.

More teeth the better

A small fly-cutter should be made to cut the ratchet teeth and the number of teeth the wheel should contain is optional. The greater the number of teeth, the more effectually will the ratchet wheel do its job. It is important that the fronts of the teeth are radial and not undercut.

The ratchet teeth on the back flange of the barrel should now be cut. They should, of course, be considerably larger than the teeth of the maintaining ratchet but an exact number of teeth does not matter. Fifty teeth is a convenient number and this number will give a nice size of tooth for this component. The fronts of these teeth are cut just undercut a few degrees. It is important that the fronts of the teeth point the right way (which is to the left or anti-clockwise when viewing the barrel from the front flange side). The great wheel and maintaining ratchet wheel can now be fitted to the barrel arbor and it is better to turn the arbor to size to fit the former rather than the other way about. Just a running fit without shake is required.

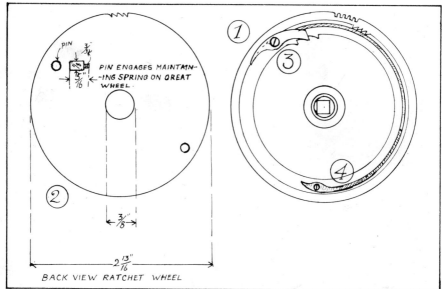

Fig. 10 Plan view of great wheel ratchet, maintaining wheel and barrel ratchet

16

The maintaining spring is shown in Fig. 9 (No. 1) in position within the sink of the great wheel. This spring is bent up from a length of 1/16 in. square silver steel. It should be just an easy fit around the hub of the inside of the great wheel. Its shorter (or eye end) holds itself against the head of a 1/8 in. dia. small screw. The height of the head should be just below the level of the great wheel hub. The free end of the spring should be made of such length to be just clear of the inside wall of the wheel.

It will be seen in the drawing that a small window is cut right through the wheel thickness. Referring to Fig. 10 (No. 2) it will be noted that there is a pin 1/8 in. dia. x 5/16 in. total length including the threaded portion. This pin protrudes from the back of the maintaining ratchet wheel into the window of the great wheel and it contacts the right hand side of the free end of maintaining spring.

Winding the spring

The effect of this is that, when there is motive power in the driving barrel, the maintaining spring is automatically wound up and the winding up is limited to the extent of about three or four teeth of the great wheel by the action of the pin reaching the left hand side of the window. As the great wheel rotates there is a click pivoted in the movement frame whose nose drops into the teeth of the maintaining ratchet wheel which is rotating with the great wheel.

In the process of winding up the driving barrel, the pivoted click will lock the maintaining ratchet wheel and at the same time the maintaining spring will expand and thus keep the great wheel rotating in an anti-clockwise direction. The drive of the maintaining spring has, of course, to be weaker than the drive of the clock weight. After the maintaining spring has been made and fitted, it should be heated up to cherry red and hardened in oil; after it has been cleaned with emery paper its temper should be let down to deep purple blue.

Making the slip washer

The next item to be made is the slip washer which is shown in the bottom left hand of Fig. 7. It should be made from a piece of 1/32 in. thick brass plate and its function is to hold the great wheel and maintaining ratchet closely to the ratchet flange of the driving barrel. A small annular groove is turned on the barrel arbor into which the sides of the slot of the slip washer will fit. When correctly positioned the slip washer has a small screw put through it into the thickness of the great wheel hub.

The barrel ratchet click, which can be of mild steel, should next be made. The plan view is shown in Fig. 9 (No. 3) and Fig. 10 (No. 3). Note it should be 1/8 in. thick and can easily be cut to shape with a metal-cutting fretsaw. Before any cutting is done, it should be drilled for its screw fixing hole with a No. 36 or 37 gauge drill, and the upper side of the hole counterbored, say, 1/32 in. deep to accommodate the head of the fixing screw whose threaded portion should be a No. 6 or 7 B.A. screw.

Locating the click

This screw will have to be made with a small shoulder between the head of the screw and its threaded portion. The click pivots on this shoulder after the screw has

17

been tightened up. Fig. 9 (No. 3a) shows what is required. An easy way to locate the position of the click in relation to the barrel ratchet is to engage its top in a ratchet tooth and place a No. 36 or 37 gauge drill upside down in the hole of the click and give a light blow with the wooden handle of the hammer to the cutting end of the drill. This is a very handy way of marking out parts that have to be fitted together. Most small drills are cone-pointed at their non-cutting ends.

Now the click spring should be made. It is seen in Figs. 9 and 10 (No. 4). It is made from a piece of stiff brass plate 3/32 in. thick and it should be carefully cut to shape with a metal-cutting fretsaw at the spoon fixed end and for a short distance beyond it, but the remainder should be cut in a straight line and bent with the fingers to the curved shape shown. Do not use pliers as these will cause kinks.

Before shaping it, it should be nicely filed up and smoothed off with emery sticks. Its position on the maintaining ratchet can be found and marked off in a similar way as was used for the click. The fixing screw for the spring is a No. 10 B.A. and it has a brass steady pin fitted at the pointed end of the spoon.

This concludes the making of the great wheel, maintaining ratchet and barrel of the time train, with the exception of the pivoting of the arbor, but this should be left until the rest of the train has been made. The other two barrels are made to exactly the same dimensions but their arbors are just left rough turned for the time being.

A point worth mentioning is that the pointed centres of all three barrel arbors must be carefully preserved from damage and must not be cut off until the clock is finished.

CHAPTER THREE

The centre and escape wheels and pinions

This chapter deals with the centre wheel, escape wheel and pinions.

The centre wheel, shown in Fig. 11 (Nos. 1 and 2), is turned to 2 in. dia. and has 96 teeth cut with the 53 dp cutter, the thickness of the wheel being approximately 1/16 in. It can be mounted on either of the wheel mandrel chucks shown earlier in Fig. 8 (Nos. 2 and 4).

The teeth are cut in a similar way to the great wheel, but as the teeth are of a finer pitch, the cutter can be passed through the blank wheel in one go. With the 52 dp cutter still in the cutter frame it is worth while machining the teeth of the third wheel which is 1/16 in. thickness and 1.76 in. dia. It has 90 teeth and is cut the same way as the centre wheel.

The next wheel in the train is the escape wheel, and the last required for the time train. It can either be purchased with its teeth already cut, or if one has a really fine slitting circular saw it can be produced in the lathe with the aid of the cutter frame. If you decide to cut it yourself, proceed as follows.

Turn a 1/16 in. brass blank to 1 13/16 in. dia., having previously mounted it on No. 4, Fig. 8 mandrel wheel chuck; next mount the slitting saw in the cutter frame and see that the saw rotates anti-clockwise, that is, towards the headstock of the lathe. Angle the cutter frame round a little so that the saw will produce an undercut cut—an angle of about 10 deg. will do very well.

Put the pointer in the 30-hole circle of the division plate and run the saw through the blank to a depth of approximately 5/32 in. There is nothing gained by

Great wheel, centre wheel, third wheel and escape wheel

going in deeper than this, for though the teeth produced may be more elgantly shaped, they are definitely weaker and easily damaged if rough handling should occur at any later date.

The cut just made is the front or acting part of the tooth. After cutting the fronts of teeth, angle the cutter frame round again for cutting the back of the tooth. It should be so manoeuvred that when the cut is made the thickness of the tip of the tooth should be approximately 6 thou. Theoretically the tips of the teeth should have not thickness at all, and some of the old makers made the tips too thin, with the result that they were easily bent or damaged. While the wheel is still on the chuck, scribe the circle representing the bases of the tooth spaces and the inner band of the wheel; also a circle for the hub of the wheel. Before dechucking the wheel the centre hole should be carefully bored to approximately 3/16 in. dia. This will ensure the teeth running true with the hole.

After dechucking the wheel the spaces between the teeth are cut out with a fine fretsaw by hand, and if this is done carefully a fine accurate escape wheel will be the result. The spaces between the spokes or arms of all three wheels should be cut with a fine fretsaw by hand, and it pays to do this cutting as accurately as possible as it will make the final filing up, which follows next, a hundred per cent. easier.

Finish off with dead smooth cut files and emery sticks. A final burnish with a steel knitting pin will give a very pleasing result.

The pinions of this clock have all been made with separate pinion heads and fitted afterwards to the arbors. Pinion wire is now almost unobtainable but the firms of Messrs. John Rigby & Sons of Cleckheaton, Yorkshire do still supply it, but it is mostly of involute form, which is not suitable to mesh with cycloidal form teeth, but the leaves can easily be reshaped with needle files to cycloidal form. Assuming pinion wire is used proceed as follows: a piece of pinion wire is cut a little longer than the distance between the outer edges of the frame plates, the two ends of the pinion wire are now filed cone shape to fit hollow centres, the filing must be carefully done so that the leaves rotate truly. Now mark on the length of the pinion wire the position of the pinion head that is to mesh with the engaging wheel, turn a nick each side where the head is to be and then file or break off the unwanted leaves, mount pinion and turn core to a fine finish, next with needle files shape the leaves to a better form (most pinion wire as supplied the leaves are not properly formed, now heat up the pinion to cherry red and plunge vertically into cold water to harden it. It has to be tempered, and a good way to do this is to dip it into oil and set it alight and let the oil burn out, it will be found that it has probably warped, this is quite an accepted fact. To bring it true again, lay the arbor on an anvil with the hollow side uppermost, now with the pane of the hammer hit the hollow side with regular strokes. This has effect of stretching the hollow side of the arbor and bringing it straight again, the pinion will now need finishing and polishing.

Another way of producing pinions is to cut them in the same way as cutting the wheels, but the cutter must rotate very much slower and the pinion head must be continually flooded with cutting oil.

A further way of making pinions is by the planing method so ably described by Mr. J.C. Stevens' article in the *Model Engineer* of June 6th 1957, an extract of which is as follows:

20

"A lever attachment is made to clamp on to the lathe bed to operate the saddle with slow powerful strokes similar to a shaping machine (see sketch) with a suitable v tool clamped to the cross slide. It is possible to cut out the spaces between the leaves providing very small cuts are taken. The tops of the leaves were finally rounded off with a small form tool as at B (sketch). It was discovered that an old flat file provided the best material for the main cutter, which undergoes considerable stress on the return stroke of the saddle, probably some improvement could be made here by hinging the cutter clapper-box fashion. It will be noticed that a special back centre was made incorporating a short angle piece provided with a hardened adjustable screw. This serves as a steady to prevent the blank deflecting outwards during cutting and proved both necessary and successful. Of course the pinion blank which is mounted between centres must be held securely to the faceplate pin. To ensure maximum rigidity during the cutting, the blank is only turned down sufficiently to expose the pinionhead and provide clearance for the cutter. The size of the arbor is reduced to size afterwards. In the hardening and tempering of silver steel it is necessary to let the temper down to white colour shade otherwise if the arbor needs straightening afterwards a fracture may occur if left too hard."

The pinions of this clock have all been made with separate pinion heads from pinion wire and fitted afterwards to the arbors. The centre pinion head is K gauge drill size .275 full by 10 leaves; cut off a piece of the wire as squarely as possible 1/2 in. in length.

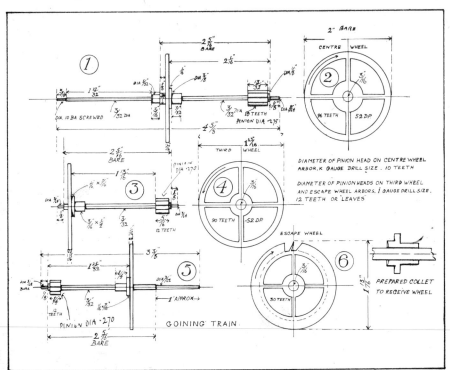

Fig. 11 Goining train

Another method

Chuck in the self-centring chuck a piece of brass rod 1/2 in. dia. x 1/2 in. in length, face off the end and drill and bore to such a size that the piece of pinion wire is a light drive-in-fit; before driving it in be sure that all burrs are removed from the ends of the pinion wire. Leave the outer end of the pinion wire protruding a little way. Held thus the pinion head can be drilled and bored true with the leaves.

Now face the protruding end of the wire dead square and centre drill the end with the slocombe drill, using only the pilot part of the drill for doing this. Next with a small drill go carefully right through the pinion head. If care is taken to feed the drill in slowly and to come out frequently to get rid of the swarf a true hole will be the result.

Looking at Fig. 11 (No. 1) it will be seen that the pinion arbor is 3/32 in. dia., so the hole in the pinion head will need enlarging by further drilling, but the final hole produced must be under 3/32 in. dia. Carefully broach out the hole with a taper broach using plenty of oil to produce a tapered hole, but the minimum amount of broaching should be done. This is important. In using the broach pull the belt of the mandrel round by hand, never do it under power. It is simply inviting accidents.

Turn the small shoulder on the pinion head, as shown in the drawing. This can easily be done with a fine knife-edge tool in the slide-rest. Pass a rod through the hollow mandrel of the lathe and knock the pinion head out of the brass bush. Chuck the pinion head the other way about and face the end off square and finish it as smoothly as possible.

The pinion head will now have to have the spaces between the leaves deepened. This can be done in the lathe with a suitable size width of slotting saw and division plate, the pinion head being mounted on a temporary mandrel between the lathe centres, or the spaces between the leaves can be treated with fine needle files, the pinion head being held in the hand or small vice. It takes a little longer doing it by hand but it is a very certain way.

Following the filing operations, the spaces between the leaves should be smoothed with fine carborundum powder and oil with the aid of a piece of end-grain hardwood shaped to go between the leaves. This will take out all the cutter and file marks.

Smooth the faces of the pinion head by rubbing them on various grades of emery sticks. The emery stick should be laid on the bench and the pinion head rubbed circular fashion taking particular care to keep it dead square with the emery stick. This will produce a remarkable finish and is not difficult to do.

Heat the pinion head over a bunsen burner to a cherry red and plunge in oil. Brighten the leaves up a little and let the temper down to a deep purple and finally polish the bottom and between the leaves with rouge and oil applied with the end-grain piece of hardwood. The pinion head is now finished.

The pinion arbor should next be made from a length of hardened and tempered steel rod about 3/32 in. dia. This rod can be obtained at most material dealers and is sold in assorted diameters. Being tempered steel it might be thought very difficult to turn in the lathe; strange as it may seem there will be no difficulty in machining it.

Turning the pinion arbor

Select a particularly straight piece of rod and cut it to a length of 4 5/8 in. Chuck it truly and turn a cone at each end. Now try the rod between hollow centres. It should rotate truly throughout its length. If it does not, select another length of rod. It must now be mounted between hollow centres and a miniature catchplate and pin made. One of the wheel mandrel chucks will do for this purpose very well. Fig. 8 (No. 3) shows what is required.

A miniature lathe carrier will also be required to fit on the rod. These miniature carriers are exactly the same in all respects (except size) as those used by engineers and are not difficult to make. The writer has one whose total length is 1/2 in. With the arbor running true between centres use the hand rest and graver and taper turn the end of the rod to fit the pinion head.

Do most of the turning with the point of the graver, resting it towards the top of the rod. It should not be at centre level as with a slide-rest tool. Heavy pressure is not needed but the point of the graver must be sharp and kept moving on the work piece. Miniature ridges will be formed with the turning but these are levelled off by using the sides of the graver for this purpose. If the rod requires further turning down the point of the graver must be used again.

If the turning has been successfully done the pinion head should fit perfectly, and by turning it to the right it can literally be screwed on the pinion arbor and no amount of pressure will shift it. As an alternative method to taper fitting the pinion heads they can be left as drilled and pressed on to a parallel rod. The rod needs very carefully turning to size. An advantage of this method over the other perhaps is that the pinion head can be shifted to a nicety to where it is wanted.

Front plate bearing

Looking at Fig. 11 (No. 1) there will be seen midway along the arbor the bearing or pivot for the front plate. This is made from a piece of silver steel round rod approximately 5/16 in. in length x 3/16 in. dia. at its shoulder and 5/32 in. dia. at the pivoted part. This stepped bush, as one might term it, should be held in the three- or four-jaw chuck and a hole drilled through of such size that the bush is a press-on fit to the arbor.

Before being pressed on the arbor it should be roughed out more or less to size on a spare piece of the blued rod between centres. The important thing to get right here is the approximate distance between the shoulders of the front and back pivot which as seen in the drawing is 2 5/16 in. bare; it would be better to leave for the present the final turning of the back pivot and do this when turning the other pivots of the train.

The collet for mounting the centre wheel should next be made. It can be a press-on fit to the arbor or soft soldered to the arbor. It should be made from cast brass rod, but as this now seems unobtainable, ordinary drawn or rolled brass rod will have to be used. A short length of 3/8 in. dia. brass rod should be drilled and turned by the same methods of the steel bush, but previously to turning the collet to size the brass rod should be heated up to almost melting point, otherwise when it comes to riveting on the wheel the brass will not spread but simply chip off.

It will be found difficult to turn both the steel bush and brass collet after they have been pressed on the centre arbor which, being so long, will be quite whippy when pressure is applied near the centre of the arbor. Some form of back stay or steady is necessary and a drawing is included to show what is required. It is quite a simple affair and must be made to suit individual lathes. The front spigot of the collet should be very carefully turned to fit the hole in the wheel.

Both the face of the flange where the wheel fits against and the face of the spigot should be turned dish-shaped, the latter rather more so to allow the metal to be riveted over the wheel. Before mounting the centre wheel to the collet it should be completely finished off and polished. It is much easier to finish before mounting than afterwards which is the usual practice.

The hole in the wheel should be slightly countersunk on both sides and a few nicks made with a file in the countersunk part where the riveting will be. This is necessary to prevent the wheel from turning round on its seating on the collet. Before the wheel is mounted a small riveting stake should be made as shown in the drawing Fig. 5 (Nos. 3 and 4). It is made from brass and comes in half; several holes of different sizes should be drilled as indicated in the drawing.

Choose a suitable size hole which should be an easy fit to the back spigot of the collet. Clamp the "stocks" in the vice and position the wheel on the front spigot of the collet and press the wheel well home against the flange of the collet.

Now the riveting can be commenced. A cut nail makes a good riveting punch. The point of the nail should be filed quite flat and reduced to about 3/32 in. dia. First rivet the metal slightly over the wheel at the due north position followed by due south, then east and west. Now take the arbor and try it between the lathe centres. If the wheel runs true edge ways finish the riveting right round the wheel. If there appears a wobble in the wheel edgeways on it can be drawn back to run true by continuing the riveting at the appropriate spot.

The metal should be made as smooth as possible with the riveting punch and it is finished by turning in the lathe either using the graver and hand-rest or it can be done with a fine knife edge tool in the slide-rest. If it should be decided to soft solder the collet on the arbor it must be made a very easy fit to allow a thickness of solder between the inner walls of the collet and the arbor.

Escape wheel

If the solder does not flow out from both ends of the collet, everlasting rust will occur no matter how well it has been washed with ammonia and water. The centre wheel and arbor should now be returned to the lathe and the back of the collet flange and spigot turned true finishing with fine emery sticks.

Attention should now be devoted to the third wheel and pinion Fig. 11 (Nos. 3 and 4) shows this completed with all the dimensions. The procedure for making it is the same method as for the centre wheel; the arbor being much shorter will make the construction much easier. It should be noted that the pinion head has 12 leaves and its diameter is 1-gauge drill size; the total length of the pinion arbor including the pivots is approximately 2 9/16 in. Do no pivoting until the escape wheel and pinion have been finished, which now follows.

The escape wheel and pinion are shown in Fig. 11 (Nos. 5 and 6). The escape wheel collet will be turned finally in situ with the aid of the steady and it is important that the wheel be mounted the correct way round. No. 6 shows the front of wheel as viewed from the front plate, the arrow indicating the rotation of the wheel which of course is clockwise.

Referring to Fig. 11 (No. 5), the front pivot that fits the hole in the front plate is turned parallel for about 1/8 in. in length and thereafter tapers off as shown in the drawing. The going train is now complete except for the pivoting which will now be described.

Fig. 12 shows the train as positioned between the plates and to get the positions of the arbors right it is expedient to lay them across the edges of the plates with the frames assembled which will show at a glance where the ends of the arbors will need turning, to form the pivots.

Referring back to the escape wheel and pinion it should be noted that the pinion head is the same diameter as the third wheel pinion head and has the same number of leaves. It can be made the same length as the third pinion head if preferred instead of 1/4 in. as shown in the drawing.

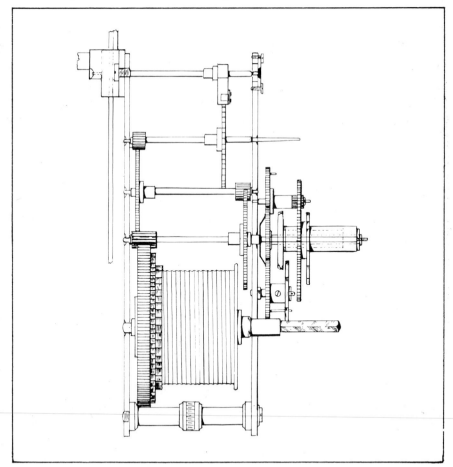

Fig. 12 Going train and motion work

CHAPTER FOUR

Pivoting, the depthing tool and the escapement

The pivoting, use of the depthing tool and the escapement are dealt with in this chapter.

Begin with the pivots of the centre arbor. The front pivot will already have been done when the steel bush was fitted to the arbor.

For the back pivot the core diameter of the arbor can be used, but the shoulder at the extreme end of the pinion head will need a little turning on its face to provide the necessary endshake of the pivots between the plates of the frame. This endshake is very important and must never be overlooked with any of the pinion arbors of the train.

Generally speaking, the pinion arbors should be run between small hollow centres with a miniature carrier attached to the forward end of the arbor. All the turning should be done at the tailstock end of the lathe. Except for large pivots such as those of the barrel I always use the hand-rest and graver. The graver is a very adaptable tool and once the knack of using it is acquired it is remarkable what one can do with it. A pivot must be turned parallel and the angle of its shoulder turned square with no likeness to the base of a lighthouse. To make a nice job of the shoulder the graver should be held as shown in the drawing.

Another help in getting a clean corner at the shoulder is to use a square chisel-shaped cutting tool. It will retain its cutting edge longer than the graver. Should the pivot glaze—which will sometimes happen if the tool becomes blunt—it can readily be removed with a fine file.

Having turned the pivot to size it should now be smoothed with a fine pivot file or needle file and polished. This is done by making a polisher from a short length of flat brass rod 3/16 in. wide x 1/16 in. thick. The left-hand edge should be bevelled

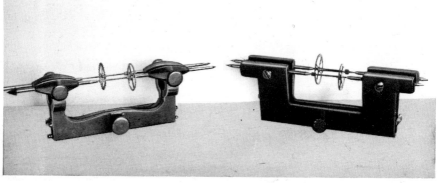

Left, commercial depth tool. Right, home-made depth tool

off and a handle fitted. The business side of the polisher should be filed to provide a bite to hold the polishing medium, which is oilstone dust mixed with oil.

Make a mixture of the oilstone dust and oil, which must not be too tin, spread it on the polisher. The polisher is then applied to the pivot with a to-and-fro motion and with a little pressure while the pivot is made to rotate fairly quickly. The polisher must be re-charged once or twice with the oilstone dust mixture, and in a very short space of time all the scratches and turnery marks will have disappeared, leaving the pivot with a smooth grey surface.

Now clean up the polisher pivot and hollow centre and charge the polisher with a mixture of crocus and oil and apply the polisher as before to the pivot and within a few minutes a well-polished pivot should result. The pivots should be finally polished with a well-oiled burnisher (I have found that the smallest size firmer chisel as used by cabinet makers makes an excellent burnisher). Do nothing at present to the pointed centres of the pivot. The third wheel and escape wheel pivots are treated in exactly the same way.

The pivots on the barrel and the great wheel should next be undertaken, the pivots being turned to fit the holes in the frame. As these have not yet been drilled, holes should be drilled in a spare piece of plate and a note made of the drills that were used. These pivots are comparatively large in diameter so they can be turned to size with a tool in the slide-rest. They should, however, be polished and burnished in a similar way to the smaller pivots, but the cone centres must still be preserved.

A depthing tool

The complete train is now ready for planting in the movement frame. Fig. 13 shows the approximate position of each wheel and pinion, but their exact arbitrary positions with one another must be obtained with the aid of a depthing tool which will now be described.

A clock depthing tool is an instrument rarely seen today but its usefulness for its particular job cannot be over-emphasised. Many substitutes have been made and suggested, but they all fall short of the genuine article. Fig. 14 shows the drawing of a depth tool which I made in a few hours. It has neither the finish nor the elegance of the genuine article, but it does its job equally well—and that is all that matters.

The main frame is made from wood. I used plywood about 3/8 in. thick, but a well-seasoned piece of beech or mahogany if available might prove better. Cut two pieces of wood 11 1/2 in. x 4 in. to form the frame. Square these up and temporarily screw them together. Now mark out the shape of the frame and screw on two fairly stiff working hinges at the appropriate position. They are better not let into the wood, but must be well in line with one another. The temporary screws can now be removed and the hinges tried out to see that there is no play.

Next the diameter of the runners must be decided. I used 1/4 in. dia. rods for these. If using that size, plane up some strips of wood 1/4 in. square section. About 4 ft of this will be required. Now place a 11 1/2 in. length of this strip along the top edge of the frame; glue and nail it where it is to be fixed. Next obtain a foot length of silver steel 1/4 in. dia. and ground rod if possible. Position the rod against the strip of wood previously fixed and now position another strip of wood against the silver steel rod, which should be nailed and glued as before. Do this to both members of the frame.

Cutting the frame

The frame should be cut out to the shape shown in the drawing (a fretsaw will do this very well). Cover strips of 1/16 in. brass will be required and should be nailed on to the previously-fixed wood strips. Following this the silver steel rod and remove all burrs from its ends and try the fit in the holes thus made. It should be a fairly stiff fit without sideplay. The sides of the frame can now be drilled and tapped to take the clamping screws for the runners, which can be made from any odd screws lying around.

Next two brass plates are screwed to the frame (see drawing). The outside plate is tapped 1 B.A. to take the adjusting screw. The inside plate takes the end thrust of the adjusting screw. A quickly-made knob for turning the adjusting screw can be made from the plastic cap of a scent bottle. The head of the screw is heated up to

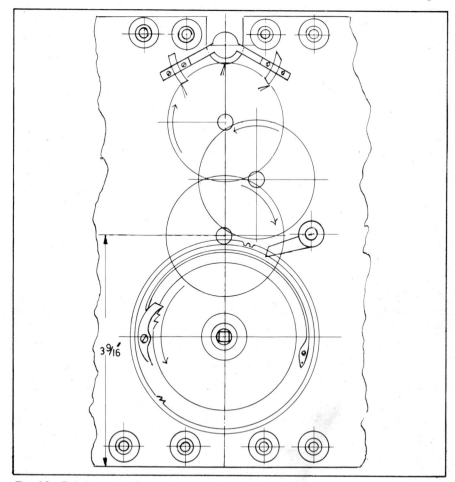

Fig. 13 Goining train, front plate removed

red and pressed into the plastic. The return spring can be made from a strip of flat section brass curtain rod, bent to a nice curve by hand. A worn-out wide hacksaw blade would do equally as well. It will be seen from the drawing that there are two retaining metal strips screwed on to the ends of the frame. These are for holding the return spring in position.

It remains only to cut some 1/4 in. dia. silver steel rod to suitable lengths to form the runners. The runners should be carefully chucked and the cone points turned. Now reverse them and drill the hollow centres with a small size slocombe drill. Extend the drilling for about 1/32 in. in each case with a No. 60 gauge drill. The runners can be inserted in their holes and the tool tested.

Using the depth tool

Screw the depth tool open a short distance and, with the pointed ends of the runners on the outside of the frame and equally in length with one another, scribe a small arc in a piece of metal. Reverse the runners and bring the pointed ends to the inside of the frame and, taking care to have their points of equal length, test them with the previously scribed arc to which they should agree. A more critical test is to try the pointed centres of runners of the other end of the depthing on the same scribed arc. Possibly the runners at this end may be out a trifle; if they are it will not matter as in using any depthing tool it is always prudent to keep to the same end of the tool for marking out—as used for testing the depth of the wheel and pinion.

Place the wheel and pinion between the hollow centres of the runners and see that they run freely but without endshake. Now adjust the screw and bring the wheel and pinion together in mesh. Their correct centres apart can be observed by viewing from the end of the depth tool, though I much prefer to rely on sound.

If they are meshed too deep or too shallow a harsh rattling sound is noticed when the wheel and pinion are spun round, whereas if they are meshed correctly a soft purring kind of sound results. There seems to be only one position where this occurs. So much depends on the shape of the teeth of the wheel and the shape of the leaves of the pinion that it appears for safer to rely on hearing than visual means.

Miniature centre punch

Assuming the correct depth has been found the wheel and pinion are taken out of the depthing tool and the clamping screws are loosened and its runners pushed in, leaving say about 3/4 in. protruding from the end of the depthing tool. The two points must then be adjusted dead level with one another.

Now make a miniature centre punch from a short length of 1/8 in. round silver steel. Harden the point and temper it down to a deep straw colour. Centre pop on the centre line of the front plate where the centre wheel will be planted. Just a tiny dot is all that is needed. Mark with a pencil the approximate position of the third-wheel pivot and with the depthing tool held in the hand—taking particular care not to squeeze it and hold it perfectly upright—scribe a small arc in the vicinity of the pencil mark.

Next take the miniature centre punch and with its point feel for the centre of the scribed arc. Give the centre punch a light tap with the hammer; the centre punch depression should be examined with a magnifying glass to make sure it is in the right position, as it is important that it must be spot on. Slightly enlarge the depression with a miniature archimedean drill, using a small spear-shape drill for the purpose. The hole can now be drilled in the drilling machine, using quite a small drill. Twist drills are quite satisfactory, but they must be taken through the metal slowly as they are hungry feeders.

Drilling procedure

It is better, though not essential, to start the drilling from inside the front plate rather than from the outside. After removing any burrs left by the drilling assemble the front to the backplate and with the same drill and using the hole in the frontplate as a jig, drill through to the backplate, but drill no more than to mark

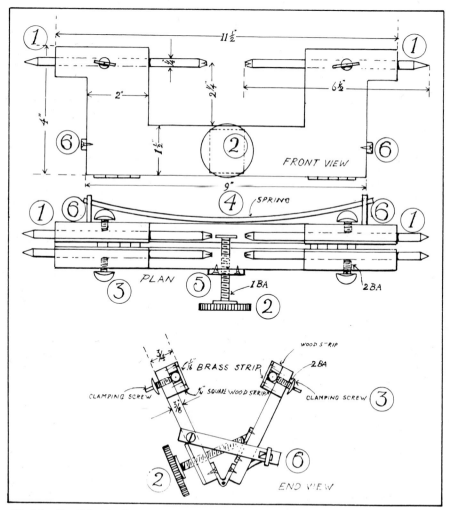

Fig.14 Depthing tool

out the position of the hole on the backplate. This is important, as otherwise the swarf that would collect between the plates would cause the drill to wander and perhaps break. So it is better to always drill the plates separately. Increase the size of the hole with larger drills, but still keeping the hole a less diameter than the pivot. Then, with a five-sided broach, broach out the hole from the inner side of the plate, using plenty of oil in the process until the pivot will go in the hole about half-way through.

Next change the broach for a round one. These can be purchased, or a knitting needle will do. Enlarge the hole with the round broach until the pivot goes home. This last bit of broaching will leave a burr on both sides of the plate, but this can easily be removed with a worn-out flat file rubbed on the plate with the fingers and thumb. The holes must be cleared of all crumbs and burrs. A hardwood peg does this quite well.

The frame can now be assembled and the run of the wheel tried out. It should spin quite freely, stopping gradually. If it stops suddenly there is something wrong. Perhaps a burr may be left on the edge of a hole, or a pivot may have a lighthouse root. The wheel and pinion should drop promptly when the frame is held in a horizontal position. These are all minor things that must be attended to in any horological work. The same process is gone through with the drilling of the hole for the third wheel and pinion. When they both spin freely in the frame they can be tried together and if the depthing has been successful a perfect result will be the outcome.

Drilling in pairs

It is expedient to mark out the position of the centre wheel and, indeed, all the wheels before doing any drilling, then the drilling can be done in pairs, the depthing tried with each pair of wheels and pinions. Should a faulty depth occur it should be rectified before going forward; to correct a faulty depth, enlarge the hole, then plug it and start again. As to the great wheel and barrel pivots, these are of a large diameter and they should not be broached with a five-sided broach as a broach of this size does not work well. A reamer can be used if available, but it will be found quite satisfactory to leave the holes just plain drilled and turn the pivots to fit the holes.

Assuming all the drilling and broaching has been successful, the complete train can be assembled and tried out. If all is right only very little pressure on the great wheel tooth should cause the escape wheel to run easily—and not stop suddenly with a jerk when the pressure is removed.

Deadbeat escapements

Fig. 15 shows the complete escapement. Although I cut a 1 13/16 in. dia. escape wheel any other smaller size wheel will do if preferred. The general directions for making the escapement will be the same.

As much has been written about the theory of deadbeat escapements it is not proposed to enter on this side of the subject. I would, however, like to give a few practical suggestions for making an escapement that will work well. Obtain a piece of 1/16 in. thick brass plate, say 3 in. x 4 in. and dull one side of the plate by rubbing pumice stone powder and water on its surface. Now mark a centre line from the top to the bottom and make a dot on the centre line for the escape wheel centre hole. Drill a hole at the dot position and fit a short brass peg, the diameter of which should be the same as that of the hole in the spare escape wheel (in cutting the teeth of the escape wheel it is better to cut two wheels together rather than separately).

Make a centre dot in the peg and with the dividers scribe a circle representing the circumference of the wheel at the tips of the teeth. Now lay the escape wheel on the plate with its peg in the centre hole of the wheel. Adjust the wheel so that the forward tip of a tooth touches the centre line on the plate and scribe round this tooth with a fine point—also scribing out the positions of the teeth marked A and B as in the drawing.

Now from the wheel centre mark out two lines each 45 deg. from the centre line on the plate. Where these lines cut through the circumference of the tips of the teeth draw tangents, and where the lines meet on the centre line on the plate will be the position of the pallet's centre. From this point with the dividers scribe an arc touching the forward side of the tip of the left hand tooth A. This will represent

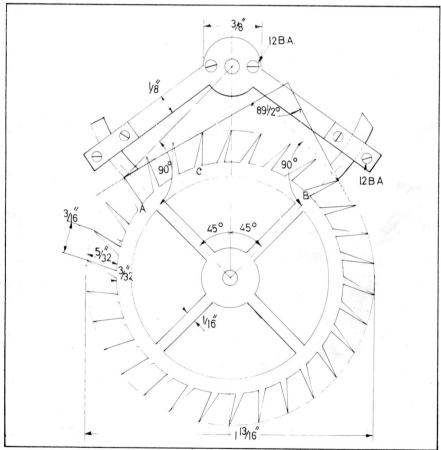

Fig.15

the resting face of the entrance pallet; a similar arc scribed on the right hand side of the drawing will represent the underside of the exit pallet.

Pallets' thickness

The thickness of the pallets has now to be decided. The thickness of each pallet equals half the distance between the tips of the adjacent teeth less a ½ deg. for drop or free run of the escape wheel. As, however, pallets usually finish by being too thin the amount to be allowed for the free run of the escape wheel can usually be neglected; so the dividers are adjusted to scribe a smaller arc in order that the thickness of each pallet equals half the distance between the tips of the wheel.
The impulse planes have now only to be scribed out and the acting part of the escapement is complete.

Obtain a small piece of thin brass sheet say 1/64 in. thick. File two sides of the brass plate to form an included angle of 89½ degrees, now adjust the brass plate so that one side intersects when the left hand resting face of the pallet and the forward tip of escape wheel tooth A meet and also where the brass plate intersects the tip of tooth C. Now adjust the other edge of the angle so that it intersects when the outer end of the right hand pallet bisects the circle representing the tip of the escape wheel tooth B.

After trying the escape wheel in the frame and being satisfied it is correct, the pallet pads should be made dead hard and not tempered afterwards but the acting surfaces must be highly polished. Scribe the lines (see drawing) which will give the impulse planes of the escapement and the arms of the yoke can be drawn in.

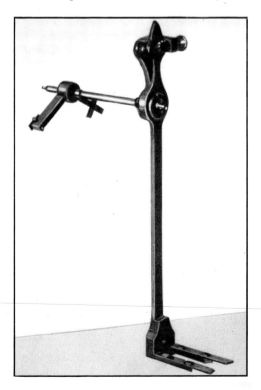

CHAPTER FIVE

The motion work

Now we come to the motion work.

Begin making the pallets by turning up in the lathe a ring from cast steel for the pallet pads. The required dimensions can be obtained from the drawing made on the brass plate; while still in the lathe its inner and outer walls can be nicely smoothed and polished.

The ring should be about 1/8 in. in depth, as indicated in Fig. 16, No. 4. After it has been finished and parted off, a small arc is cut off for each pallet pad. A quicker way to make the pads, to which the professional horologist would not agree, is to file up a piece of silver steel to the correct section and bend to a curve to fit the drawing. This has been tried and works well.

The yoke should next be made which can be of steel or brass. Mount a circular blank of 3/16 in. in thickness in the wheel mandrel. Chuck and turn the circular channel or sink to hold the pallet pads. It should be turned slightly less than 1/8 in. in depth so that the pallet pads are just proud of the surface of the yoke. Contrary to expectations, it is better to turn the channel sufficiently large so that the pads will be an easy fit. This is necessary otherwise it is impossible to adjust them in the channel.

While in the lathe drill the centre hole to fit the pallet arbor; just a nice push-on fit is required. Now cut the yoke to shape as shown in Fig. 15. Follow this by drilling and tapping the holes to take the fixing screws for the retaining strips which are made from 1/32 in. steel. When screwed down these retaining strips will hold the pads quite securely in the channel of the yoke. The two holes to take the screws to fasten the yoke to the collet will also require drilling.

The correct impulse angle on the pads should now be filed and finished with various grades of emery sticks. It is important when finishing the impulse planes to keep the corners of the pads quite sharp and not rounded, but a very slight imperceptible hump in the centre of the impulse plane can be an advantage. If the final polishing is done by hand this will be automatically produced.

The pallets can now be assembled and the yoke screwed to the pallet collet, tried out in the depthing tool and the adjustments made. Looking at Fig. 15 it will be seen that the tip of tooth A of the escape wheel has reached the extreme outside corner of the left hand pad. This is the entrance pallet.

With the swing of the pendulum the tip of the tooth will travel for a short distance along the outer circular side of the pad during which no movement of the escape wheel will occur. On the return swing of the pendulum the tip of the tooth will glide back again, but even so the escape wheel will not have rotated.

Eventually, however, the tip of the tooth will reach and glide across the impulse plane of the pad causing the yoke to swing to the left and bring the inner dead wall

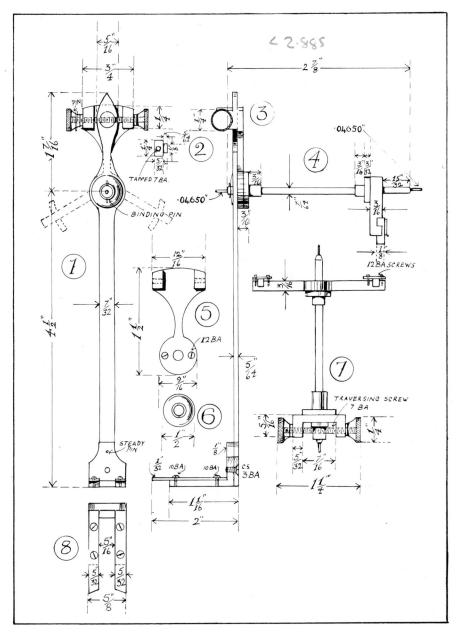

Fig.16   Constructional details of adjustable pendulum crutch

of the right pad called the exit pallet in the path of the tip of the tooth marked B.

Before the tip of the tooth reaches the pad the escape wheel will have a very small amount of free run or lead, horologically known as drop. The art of adjusting this escapement is to endeavour to get this free run of the wheel down to a minimum. The tips of the teeth must contact the extreme corners of the circular dead faces of the pads in each case.

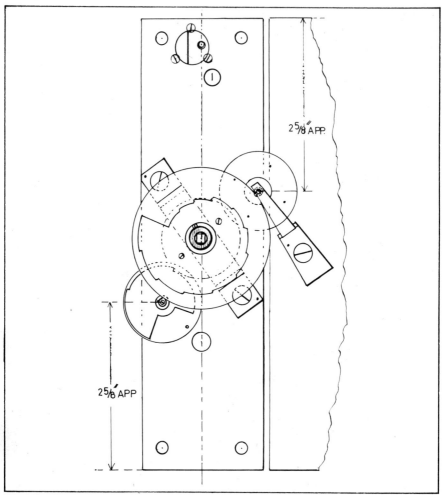

Fig.17   Motion work assembled on front plate

By constructing the escapement in the way described it will be seen there is scope to carry out the adjustments required. The front pivot of the pallet arbor should be planted in a novable bush in the frontplate so that it can be raised or lowered as required. Having tried the action of the escape wheel and pallets in the depthing tool their centres apart should be transferred to the clock plates.

Before scribing off the pallets, pivot the centre on the movable bush. It should be made as shown in Fig. 17, No. 1. Here again the bush should be made an easily turned fit in the hole of the plate otherwise fine adjustment cannot be done. It is held in position by the three large headed specially made 10 B.A. screws.

Using the pivot hole in the bush as a jig, mark the position on the back or pillar plate of the movement. Enlarge the hole so that the pallet arbor is just an easy fit. Eventually a piece of the backplate will be cut away but for the moment this hole should remain so that the escapement can be tested and adjusted if necessary.

The pendulum cock is the next item to be made. Fig. 18 shows several views of

36

this component. It is made of brass. No. 1 shows its plan viewed as it would be fixed to the outside of the backplate. The angle sides should be made from angle brass. The connecting bridges should be silver soldered to the two angle sides and it is worth while pinning the pieces together with brass pins before the soldering operations.

If hard soldering is not possible soft solder will do, but in that case brass screws must be used instead of the pins and it should be screwed up tight before the solder sets. A large file fixed in the vice and the workpiece rubbed on the file is a comfortable and fascinating way of getting good flat surfaces and square edges.

From a piece of 3/8 in. dia. brass rod make the supporting arms for the trunnion of the pendulum suspension. On each of the arms is turned a short spigot equal in length to the thickness of the bridge piece of the cock. The spigots should be threaded with a 1/4 in. x 40 thread die and the thread must be taken right up to the shoulder of the rod.

Next, the bridge piece is drilled and tapped to suit the screwed rods which should be screwed well home and each one marked to its respective position. The ends of the screwed portions should be slotted as shown in view No. 4, so that the arms can be unscrewed without damage. Half the rod in each case is cut away as seen in Nos. 1, 2 and 4, leaving a distance apart of 9/16 in., which corresponds with the distance apart of the shoulders on the trunnion of the pendulum.

A V-shaped groove should be filed out as shown in Nos. 2 and 3. No. 3 shows the side view of the pendulum cock and No. 4 the plan view looking from the front of the movement plate. It is better to leave the turning of the back pivot of the pallet arbor until the cock is finished. It can then be easily marked off for the correct length between the shoulders allowing say 1/64 in. for end play.

To position the pendulum cock on the backplate, insert the front pivot of the pallet arbor in the hole on the movable bush. The core of the pallet arbor will pass through the hole in the backplate. The pendulum cock should now have the pivot hole drilled and broached to fit the back pivot of the pallet arbor. The back pivot is then inserted in the pendulum cock which can now be nicely adjusted for correct position. Be sure to keep the cock horizontal with the clock plates.

The holes for the retaining screws should have been first drilled in the cock and backplate and the latter tapped for the screws. When satisfied that the position is correct screw the cock home and drill and fit steady pins as shown in the drawing. There is a right and wrong way of fitting steady pins. Drill the holes right through both the cock and backplate while they are still screwed together.

Separate them and broach out the holes from the front of the cock. File up some steady pins in the lathe so that the fit of the taper end just protrudes from the inner side of the cock. Next make a small countersink on the inner side of the cock to each hole. A round nose dental burr is excellent for doing this.

A similar countersink should be made to the two holes in the backplate. Resting the cock on the wheel riveting stake, drive in the two prepared steady pins so that their smaller ends protrude 1/8 in. Finally broach out the holes in the backplate a trifle and the fit of the back cock should be perfect with no play, yet easily removed. When required the U-shape slot in the backplate can now be cut away and fine finished.

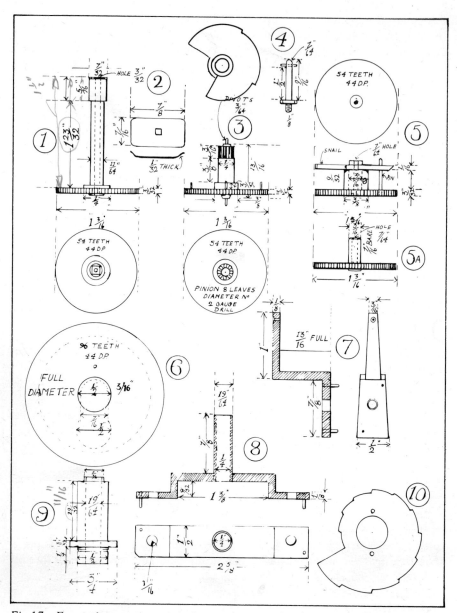

Fig.17a Front plate motion work dissembled

Fig. 16 shows the adjustable crutch complete in all parts. No. 1 shows the front view and the main flat rod. In the normal run of longcase clocks this rod is bent with the fingers to adjust the pallet pads to the escape wheel teeth to make the pendulum tick evenly, actually rather a crude method; but with this adjustable crutch the clock can be brought into beat to a nicety.

To return to the main flat rod, this has provision for rotating it slightly, and its centre of rotation is on the same axis as the pallet arbor. At its base it will be noted

that there is screwed to the rod at right angles a fork whose arms embrace the pendulum rod.

The upper end of the swinging rod is cut spear-shape and near the top in a central position there is a small stud which can rotate slightly where it passes through a hole in the spear. This stud is cross tapped as seen in the drawing. A traverse 7 B.A. screw threads into the tapped hole of the stud.

The ends of the traverse screw pass through two plain holes cross drilled in the two lugs situated on the upper end of a brass quadrant. The brass quadrant is screwed to the flange of a brass collet which in turn is soft soldered to the pallet arbor.

Two knurled heads or nuts are fixed to the ends of the traverse screw, one of which is a fixture to the screw and the other has a cross pin put right through the knurled head and traverse screw.

No. 2 shows the stud with the cross-tapped 7 B.A. hole; its spigot end is just a rotating fit in the hole of the spear-shaped arm and needs no fixing as the traverse screw will hold it in position. No. 4 is a side view of the adjustable crutch complete with the escapement seen at the right-hand end of the arbor. No. 3 is the end view of one of the adjustable nuts which should be knurled. No. 5 is the brass quadrant showing the cross-drilled lugs at the top.

Soldering the lugs

It will be found quite easy to silver solder the two lugs to the quadrant but they should first be pinned to prevent movement during the soldering. A mere speck of solder to each lug is all that is required. The less solder the easier it will be to clean up afterwards.

No. 6 is a brass retaining washer. It is made convex on the outside with a small flat in the centre and hollowed out on the underside. There is a cross binding pin put through the pallet arbor which holds the main flat rod close to the quadrant.

No. 7 represents a plan view from above, showing pallets and adjusting nuts. No. 8 is a plan view from above the fork or crutch proper. This is made from angle brass about 3/32 in. thick. It is screwed and steady pinned to the main flat rod. The slot of the fork should be carefully cut slightly over 5/16 in. in width, as it is almost impossible to file the inner sides of the fork truly parallel one with the other.

A small slip of steel is screwed to one arm, its inner side in line with the inner edge of the fork. A similar piece of steel is screwed on the other arm but the clearance holes for the screws are elongated, a trifle to allow for adjustment of this steel strip. There should be only just perceptible play between the arms of the crutch and the pendulum rod.

The parts of the adjustable crutch can now be assembled. The collet should be soft soldered to the pallet arbor as before mentioned. The hole in the quadrant is just a push-on fit to the pallet arbor and it is held to the collet by two 12 B.A. countersunk screws.

The main flat rod comes next in position, its hole being the same size as the hole in the quadrant. This is followed by the brass washer, which has a nick filed across the flat central portion. The pallet arbor will now require cross drilling to take the pin as shown. A No. 65 gauge drill will be the right size for the diameter of the pin.

39

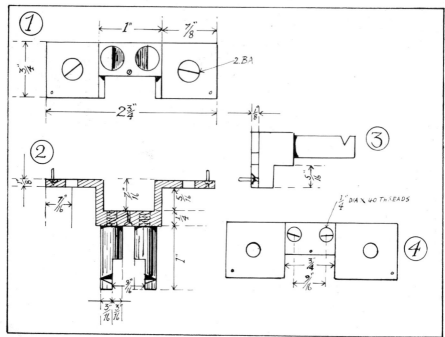

Fig.18   Details of pendulum cock

When all is pinned up the main flat rod should rotate without play.

A few hints on cross drilling of small holes in steel arbors may perhaps be acceptable. Commence by filing a small, flat nick where the drilled hole is to take place. Now either grip the arbor in a small machine vice or seat it in a miniature V-block. With the miniature centre punch, centre pop a dot on the flat nick.

Take the miniature archimedean drill and with a small pear-shape drill enlarge the dot considerably. With the appropriate drill in the drill press and the arbor held level in the machine vice it will be found that the drill will follow the countersunk depression and not wander off sideways.

Feed the drill slowly and take care when the point of the drill breaks through the underside of the arbor. The collet to which the yoke of the escapement is fixed should not be soldered to the pallet arbor, but should have a small screw put through the thickness of the flange of the collet to clamp it to the arbor. This will allow the escapement to be set roughly in beat before using the adjustable crutch.

The 7 B.A. traverse screw can now be assembled and the removable knurled nut screwed home and locked with its cross pin. There must be no backlash and the action should work with some stiffness. Before completing the going train there remains the motion work situated on the outside of the centre frontplate. This will next be described.

The motion work is shown in Fig. 17 and again in Fig. 12. Fig. 17a shows the various parts of its construction. Referring to Fig. 17 it will be noted that there are three minute wheels. The centre one, drawn in dotted lines is concentric with the centre wheel of the train and drives the upper minute wheel situated on the right-hand side of the frontplate.

This minute wheel has four lifting pins inserted in its front face for operating the quarter chimes. Also concentrically fixed to the arbor of this minute wheel is a pinion of eight leaves which drives the hour wheel of 96 teeth.

The lower minute wheel situated on the left-hand side of the frontplate is also driven by the centre minute wheel. This wheel carries the quarter snail. Fig. 12 shows clearly a side view of the motion work.

The bridge on which the hour wheel is positioned is drawn broken and the minute cock of the upper minute wheel has been left out for clarity reasons.

First a small square should be filed on the front pivot of the centre arbor just above where it emerges through the frontplate. It must not be more than say 1/32 in. deep. Make the friction spring (Fig. 17a, No. 2); it can either be a piece of clock spring or a piece of hardened brass. The square in the centre should fit the square on the centre arbor.

The three minute wheels should next be cut. They each contain 54 teeth and are cut with a No. 44 dp cutter. Although their thickness is shown to be all the same, the centre minute wheel could with advantage be made of 1/8 in. thickness as when in position it has to have a certain amount of end play on account of the elasticity of the friction on which it butts. There are no spokes or arms to the minute wheels.

Fixing the minute wheel

Referring to Fig. 17a, No. 5a the lower minute wheel has been drawn again to show it without the quarter snail and tube which is superimposed over the minute wheel tube. Now looking at No. 1 it will be noted that this minute wheel is fixed at the end of a long tube. This tube should be made of brass and its hole should be a running fit on the front pivot of the centre arbor.

It is more expedient to do the drilling first on account of the length of the hole; the outside of the tube can then be turned true with the drilled hole, a seating for which should now be turned and in this instance the wheel should be soft soldered on to the seating.

Make a small chamfer on the edge of the hole in the wheel for the solder to run into. Do the soldering over the bunsen burner. The upper end of the tube is made with an enlarged boss on the upper end of which is eventually filed a square 1/32 in. in height. This should not be done for the present.

No. 3 is the next item to be made. Commence by making its arbor from a piece of 1/8 in. dia. silver steel. Make the pinion head from a piece of No. 2 drill gauge pinion wire which has eight leaves. The pinion head should be drilled to size to be a press fit on the arbor. The leaves should be deepened and shaped if necessary, but there is no need to harden this pinion head.

Next a short piece of brass rod to form the collet should be drilled through to fit the arbor and soft soldered to it, taking care not to let the solder wander up the leaves of the pinion. The arbor with a small carrier attached should be placed between centres and a seating turned for the wheel. The wheel in this case is better riveted to the collet.

The four lifting pins should be put in the wheel later, when the chiming construction work is being done. Before turning the pivots the minute cock shown at No. 7 should be undertaken. It is made from brass angle and will require the upper member silver soldering to the angle brass.

This fitment can be filed up and finished the same way as the pendulum cock. By clamping it to the edge of the frontplate the correct distance apart of the shoulders of the pivots of the pinion arbor to the minute wheel can be ascertained. Always allow a trifle for end shake.

No. 5 shows the lower minute wheel; this rotates on a stud situated on the left-hand side of the frontplate, see Fig. 17. Looking at 5a it will be noted that this wheel is mounted on a brass tube. This brass tube is made by carefully drilling up a short length of 3/16 in. dia. rod. The hole should be a running fit on the stud.

The hour wheel

It is better to fit the stud to the hole in the tube rather than vice versa. To make the stud, chuck a short length of 1/4 in. dia. mild-steel rod in the self-centring chuck. Turn the end down to a diameter and length of 1/8 in. and run the 1/8 in. x 40 thread die along the spigot.

The die should be reversed in the die holder and the thread finished to the extreme corner of the shoulder. Now de-chuck the piece of rod and screw it into the previously prepared and tapped hole to receive it. Before this can be done the relative position with the centre minute wheel must be ascertained and marked out with the depth tool.

The hour wheel (Fig. 17a, No. 6) contains 96 teeth and is cut by the 44 dp cutter, its full diameter being 2 3/16 in. It is made from a 1/16 in. thick brass disc and has a 1/2 in. hole bored centrally through it. It fits the step on the hour wheel tube (Fig. 17a, No. 9), its position being on the underside of the flange of the hour tube, and it is held friction tight to the face of the flange by a large slip washer slightly domed and about 1/32 in. thick.

It is of a similar type to the slip washer on the arbor of the great wheel and barrel of the going train but larger. A separate drawing has not been made for this item but the hatched lines show all that is required in No. 6.

View showing time train, left hand front plate removed

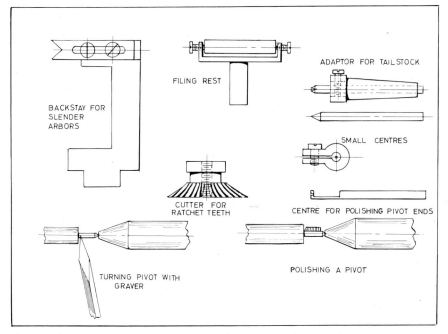

Fig 19   Some appliances required for making the clock

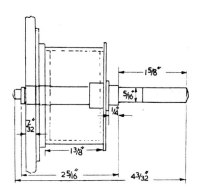

Fig. 20   Further details with clearer
dimensions of the barrel arbor

CHAPTER SIX

The hour bridge

The hour bridge and the depthing of the hour wheel are among the items detailed here.

To make the hour bridge cut two pieces of 1/8 in. thick angle brass to the sizes shown in the drawing Fig. 17a, No. 8.

Pin and silver solder the connecting bridge piece. Now file up and true it, taking care that the bases of the feet are flat and true with one another. Now make a centre pop in the centre of the bridge piece and drill two holes in the feet for the fixing screws and mount the bridge on a prepared disc of wood screwed to the faceplate of the lathe. Bring up the tailstock centre to the centre-popped depression on the bridge and tighten the woodscrews in the feet of the bridge.

Now drill to size and thread the hole with a 5/16 in. x 40 thread tap and take particular care to keep the tap in line with the lathe centres. From a short length of 5/16 in. brass rod prepare and thread one end with the 40 thread by 5/16 in. die. Screw the rod into the threaded hole in the bridge quite tight as a permanency and test for centricity; if out a little it can be turned true.

Centre drill the end with a slocombe in the tailstock and drill and bore out to approximately 1/4 in. diameter so that the hole clears the boss on the centre minute wheel tube. Now support the free end of the tube with the tailstock centre and turn down the outside to 19/64 in. so that the hour tube is a running fit.

While still on the faceplate a light skin over the surface of the bridge is advisable, making sure that there is no lighthouse root left around the junction of the tube and the bridge. Smooth off and polish the outside of the tube as the hour tube has to revolve on the bridge tube. It can now be detached from the faceplate.

The hour wheel tube (Fig. 17A, No. 9) should be made from a short length of 3/4 in. dia. brass rod. It should first be chucked and the hole drilled and bored a running fit on the tube of the hour wheel bridge just completed.

If the rod is gripped in the chuck with sufficient of it protruding from the chuck jaws the boring of the hole and turning of the outside diameter can all be done at one setting. The two spigots on each side of the flange should taper very slightly towards the outer ends of the tube. This will facilitate the mounting of the hour wheel and snail.

The extreme upper end of the hour tube should be turned down to approximately 11/32 in. in diameter to accommodate the hour hand. The snail No. 10 which will be made later butts against the upper face of the flange and is held thereto by two 10 B.A. countersunk screws positioned diametrically opposite each other. Looking at Fig. 17A, No. 5 again it will be seen that the quarter snail is riveted to a tube that fits over the tube to which the minute wheels are riveted. There is a setscrew for clamping the outer tube to the wall of the inner tube which is indicated in the drawing No. 5.

The cutting of the steps on the quarter snail and the pin in the minute should be left alone for the present.

The depthing of the hour wheel with the leaves of the pinion of the arbor of the upper minute wheel should now be done. It will be necessary in the case of the hour wheel tube to turn a short length of brass rod to fit the interior diameter of the tube. The piece of rod must be cone pointed at each end. The pinion will be a driver and it will be found to work very easily with the right engagement of the hour wheel teeth.

The hour wheel and tube should now be removed from the depth tool without altering the setting of the arms of the depth tool. Insert in the depth tool the centre minute wheel and upper minute wheel. They should mesh perfectly together and the same with the lower minute wheel. As all the three minute wheels have the same number of teeth there is a little more latitude regarding depthing which is not present in the hour wheel and pinion on minute wheel arbor.

The depths can now be scribed off on the frontplate, taking care to adjust the length of the runners of the depth tool so that the tool remains perfectly upright during the scribing operation. It will be noted that the upper minute wheel pivot is held by a cock which is screwed and steady pinned to the right-hand frontplate and not the frontplate of the going train. Care must be taken that this wheel runs truly upright when the cock is screwed home in position.

The lower minute wheel rotates on a short stud. This will have been partially made. A hole 3/32 in. in diameter at the depth position scribed on the front plate should now be drilled and threaded with the 1/8 in. Whitworth tap. Before turning

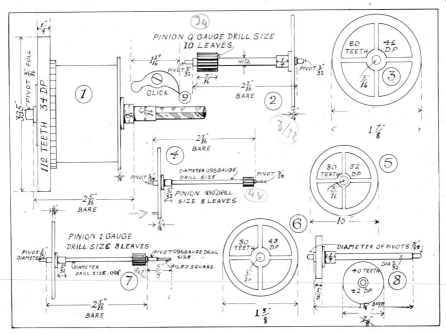

Fig.21 Working drawings of chiming and striking train

the upper spigot of the stud the steel rod should be screwed well home in the hole in the plate. The screwed end must be nicely rounded off and polished—on no account must the screwed ends of any studs be allowed to project beyond the thickness of the plates. The stud should now be cut roughly to length and a cone point is turned on the end. It can be held in the self-centring chuck by the screwed end or by the piece of the rod that will form the flange, the outer end being steadied by the tailstock hollow centre. With light cuts it should be turned down quite parallel to 7/64 in. diameter to be a running fit to the minute wheel tube. The stud is drilled to take a crosspin as shown in the drawing.

The going train is now complete and all the various parts should be made smooth and polished with emery sticks of various grades starting with a No. 2 grade and finishing with 0.000. This latter grade polishes much better after it has been in use some time.

The wisdom of making the pendulum first rather than the movement will now be appreciated. Should the making of the movement have taken place first there would have been the temptation to construct a temporary crude pendulum to see if the clock would go. Given a pendulum of good construction any faults must be looked for elsewhere.

The elimination of all crumbs, swarf, filings and, in particular, any burrs around the pivot holes, is absolutely essential for proper performance of the movement. As the making of the weights and pulleys has not yet been described a temporary weight of, say, four or five pounds on a single line should be enough to drive the barrel.

A small hole as shown in Fig. 6 should be drilled through the barrel close to the right-hand side of the barrel ratchet for the reception of the driving line. A large hole is also drilled in the face of the ratchet flange so that a knot can be tied to prevent the line pulling out of the small hole in the barrel. All the pivot holes will require oil; also the escape wheel teeth and just a spot on the fork of the crutch, but *no* oil should be allowed on the leaves of the pinions or teeth of the wheels.

The chiming and striking train

It will be remembered that the driving barrel was made at the same time as the time-driving barrel, and it has the same size diameter of arbor on which the great wheel has to be a running fit. The chiming and striking great wheel is made in exactly the same way as the time great wheel.

Looking at Fig. 21, No. 1, it will be noted that the full diameter of the blank is approximately 3 3/8 in. There are 112 teeth and the thickness of the blank is 1/4 in. Both sides of the blank should just be skimmed true, and the cutting of the teeth should be done in two stages; the first cut taking the bulk of the metal away, and the second or finishing cut should be a light one. This will help to produce nice clean teeth without chatter marks. Always feed the cutter with a feedscrew action, and not with a rack or lever feed.

There is no recess required in this great wheel. It is held on the barrel arbor with a slip washer which is exactly the same as the slip washer of the time barrel.

Next follows the click. This item is shown in No. 9; it is larger than the time barrel click, as it has to withstand more pressure. Its thickness, which is not shown in the drawing, is approximately 5/32 in. It is pivoted on a screw in just the same way as that of the time great wheel, the threaded portion being No. 5 B.A. and the shoulder being 5/32 in. in diameter. It is important that these clickscrews be well tightened home and yet leave the click to pivot easily on the shoulder of the screw.

The brass spring for the click is the same in all respects as that of the time train. The pivoting of the barrel arbor had better be left until the rest of the train has been made.

The second wheel—Fig. 21, No. 2 and No. 3 show this item—the diameter of this wheel is 1 7/8 in., and it is cut with 42 dp cutter and contains eighty teeth. The thickness of the blank is shown as 1/16 in.; it could, however, with advantage be 3/32 in. in thickness, as it has to withstand quite a bit of pressure. The pinion head contains ten leaves, and should be made from a piece of Q-gauge drill size pinion wire. As it is a large pinion it can be bored taper with a miniature boring tool in preference to using a taper broach. The leaves should be shaped, and the spaces between the leaves deepened a little for clearance of the great wheel teeth. Its pivots are approximately 3/32 in. in diameter.

Great wheel and barrel of musical train

The next items to put in hand are the pallet wheel and pinion. Fig. 21, Nos. 6 and 7, give details of these. The wheel blank is 1/16 in. in thickness, and its diameter is 1 5/8 in. It contains eighty teeth and is cut with a 48 dp cutter. The pinion head is No. 1 gauge drill size, and it has eight leaves. (It will be noted from the drawing that the front pivot extends through the front plate and has a square filed on the end of the pivot.)

It is well to keep the front pivot as large in diameter as possible, so as to be able to produce a square on its end of reasonable size. The total length of the front pivot is a good 5/8 in.

The warning wheel is shown in Fig. 21, Nos. 4 and 5. The wheel is 1 1/2 in. in diameter by 1/16 in. thick. It contains eighty teeth and is cut with a No. 52 dp cutter. Its pinion head has eight leaves and the diameter is No. 12 gauge drill size. It should be remembered that there is a pin near the rim of the wheel of about 1/32 in. diameter.

A spigot should be made in the fitting end of this pin and after it has been fitted to the wheel, it should be well riveted. Never drive a pin into a wheel and hope for the best. It will surely loosen sooner or later.

The next item on the list to be made is the reversing wheel, and the wheel that is fixed to the chiming and striking arbor. The former is seen in Fig. 21, No. 8, and the latter is shown in Fig. 22, No. 5. They are about half the size in diameter of the second wheel and each contains forty teeth and is cut with the 42 dp cutter. They both should be a full 1/8 in. in thickness; in fact the one that is fixed on the chiming and striking arbor could be 3/16 in. in thickness.

Apart from the chiming and striking barrel (which will be described separately) the fly is the last item of the train. Fig. 22, Nos. 1 and 2 show the fly and its dimensions. The pinion head has eight leaves and the diameter is 17 drill gauge size. It will be seen that a spigot has to be turned down on the arbor at the opposite end to that of the pinion head. Some form of steady must be rigged up on the lathe to prevent the arbor from whipping during the turning. If preferred—instead of turning the arbor down to produce a shoulder—a small bush made from steel can either be pressed on the arbor or soft soldered in position. This will do equally well.

Fig. 22, Nos. 2 and 3 shows the construction of the cross member with the two vanes. All this part of the fly is made from brass and it should be kept as light as possible. The tube part should be drilled a running fit on the spigot of the arbor, and it is just riveted to the cross member. The vanes are made from thin brass sheet, say 1/64 in. thick, and are soft soldered into the studs, a fine saw cut being made in

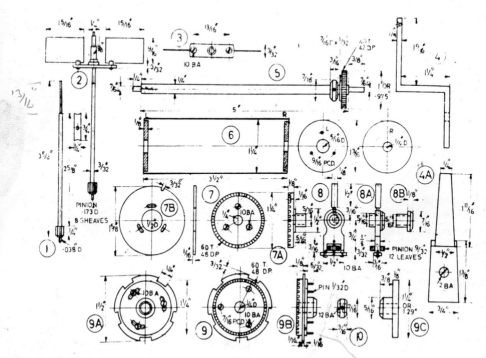

Fig. 22 The fly, vanes, fly-cock and parts of the chiming gear

the latter to accommodate them. A mere speck of solder is all that is necessary and the soldering operations are best carried out over the flame of the bunsen burner.

It would, perhaps, be as well to state here that it is far better practice to have a fly with large vanes rather than small ones. Large vanes have the effect of steadying the run of the train, and during the chiming this is of special importance. With an eight-hammer chime it means a somewhat heavier driving weight, but this does no harm with strong great wheel teeth, such as are being used in this clock.

The studs and vanes work on shoulders and after being adjusted are tightened with two 10 B.A. screws put through the holes from the underside of the cross member. This is better practice than riveting the studs a stiff fit to the cross member which is the usual way. If riveted the studs soon loosen after being adjusted a few times.

It will be seen there is a thin brass or steel spring placed between the shoulder of the pinion arbor and the underside of the cross member. Its half-circular ends which butt against the heads of the 10 B.A. screws prevent it from moving out of position. The spigot of the arbor will require cross-drilling with a small hole to take the pin which holds all together. The purpose of the spring is to allow the cross member and vanes to rotate slightly after the pinion arbor has come to rest..

Fig. 22, items No. 4 and 4a show two views of the fly cock. It should be built up and silver soldered together and is better finished before the fly pinion arbor pivots are turned.

CHAPTER SEVEN

The musical train

The items which make up the musical train are perhaps the more complicated components of the movement to make, but if the drawings are carefully studied there should not be any difficulty. In Fig. 23 is a front view of the barrel and the wheels of the train in position in the movement frame. And in Fig. 22 will be seen details of the working drawings of its various parts.

Referring to Fig. 23, it should be noted that the great wheel drives the second pinion. The second wheel, besides driving the pallet wheel pinion, also drives the reversing wheel, and the reversing wheel in turn drives a similar wheel permanently attached to the chiming arbor.

Now referring again to Fig. 22, there will be seen the chime wheel at the end of the arbor. A collet is fixed to its arbor and this gear is riveted to it. To the left of the chime wheel is a set collar fitted with a binding screw. This collar is for adjusting the end shake of the chime barrel itself.

The next item on the arbor is the chime barrel, which is a revolving fit on the arbor and is not fixed in any way. At the left-hand end of the barrel, and attached to it is a disc of brass whose function will be explained later. Beyond the disc is a contrate wheel of 60 teeth. This wheel is screwed firmly to the end of the barrel with the disc interposed.

The fixed arm is screwed to the chime arbor and at all times rotates with the latter. This arm carries a pinion of 12 leaves which mesh with the teeth of the contrate wheel attached to the chime barrel.

On the arbor is another contrate wheel, the same in all respects as the previous one. This contrate wheel also meshes with the pinion in the fixed arm. There are screwed to the back of the contrate wheel two discs; the larger disc has five notches around its circumference, and the smaller one has five equally spaced pins projecting at right angles from the side of the disc. This last contrate wheel with the two discs attached to it, is a revolving fit on the chime arbor.

Next follows another set collar and binding screw. To the left of the contrate wheel this collar is just a nice sliding fit on the arbor, and can be made either of phosphor bronze or hard brass. Note that the sides of the collar are chamfered.

Referring to Fig. 22 again, No. 6 is the chime barrel, Nos. 7 and 7a the chime contrate wheel, No. 7b the disc with a notch in its circumference, Nos. 8, 8a and 8b the fixed arm. Nos. 9, 9a, 9b and 9c show the second contrate wheel and the two discs. No. 10 gives details of the two set collars.

Figs. 24, 25 and 26 show the completed chiming and striking barrels and the arbor. The arbor should be made from a length of silver steel, and if a ground piece of rod is used, the main body of the arbor should require no turning.

The chime barrel is composed of a brass tube 1/16 in. thick x 1 1/4 in. dia., and

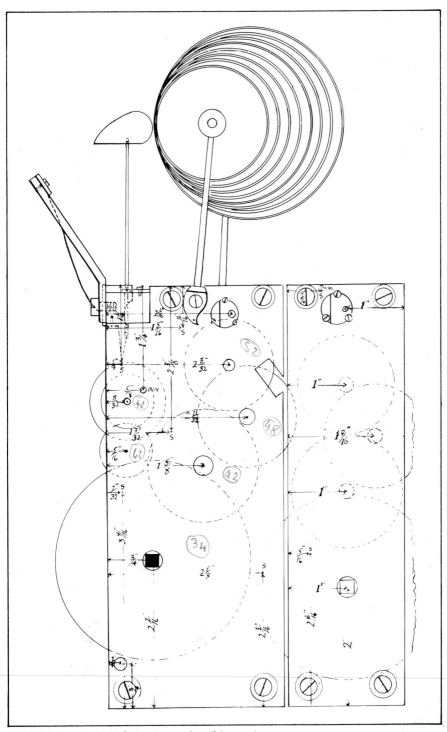

Fig.23   Front view of chiming and striking train

should have brass discs 1/8 in. thick fitted and soft soldered into both ends of the tube, followed by centrally boring in each disc a hole 1/4 in. dia. This can be conveniently done by gripping each end of the tube in the chuck and supporting the other end in a three-point steady. It should be finally fixed on a spare mandrel between centres and skimmed true.

The two contrate wheels should next be made. Nos. 7 and 7a give details of the contrate wheel to be attached to the chime barrel; a short piece of hard brass rod 1 1/4 in. dia. should be truly chucked with 1/2 in. protruding from the chuck jaws. (This diameter is slightly under the size required, but will do perfectly well). The rod should be faced off true and a sink turned 3/32 in. deep, leaving a rim with a thickness of slightly less than 1/16 in. It is also expedient to bevel the inside edge of the rim a trifle.

A central hole should be smoothly bored 1/4 in., to be a running fit on the chime arbor. At this stage the contrate teeth should be cut. The wheel contains 60 teeth and is cut with a 48 dp cutter. The cutter is set up in the cutter frame horizontally, dead on centre line with the lathe centres, and the cutter is fed across the face of the blank with the cross-slide feedscrew, taking care not to run the cutter into the farther side of the rim of the wheel.

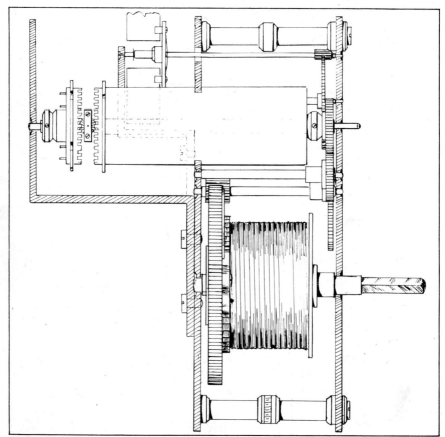

Fig.24   Side view of chiming and striking train

Next, the spigot at the back of the wheel is turned without de-chucking the wheel. The total thickness of the wheel itself should be 1/8 in., and the spigot is made 5/16 in. dia. A small, raised boss shown at the rear of wheel is not absolutely essential, as the hole in the disc that butts against the back of the wheel can also be turned 5/16 in. dia. The wheel and the spigot are finally parted off from the rod, leaving the spigot a trifle over 5/16 in. in length.

Three equidistant holes are now drilled in the contrate wheel to take three 10 B.A. countersunk screws, which are screwed into the end of the chime barrel. The interposing disc No. 7b is a simple matter, as it is just a brass disc 1/16 in. thick, and has three circular slots near its centre hole through which the 10 B.A. screws pass, so arranged that the disc can be rotated slightly for adjustment purposes.

There is a notch filed in the rim of the disc, but this is better done after the pins have been put in the barrel.

The fixed arm

This item is shown in Fig. 22, Nos. 8, 8a, and part of it in 8b. The main body is cut from 1/8 in. brass plate; the hole is bored 5/16 in. dia., and to this hole a phosphor-bronze bush is fitted which should be a press-in fit. The bush is bored 1/4 in. dia. to be a good sliding fit on the chime barrel arbor.

A steel screw is made with a long head, the threaded portion being 8 B.A., the purpose being to clamp the arm firmly to the chime barrel arbor. At the other end of the arm a slot is cut and a cross member fitted and screwed into position with two 10 B.A. screws.

In this window thus formed, a pinion of 12 leaves is pivoted. The diameter of this pinion is 9/32 in. The length of the right end of the phosphor-bronze bush is turned down so that the pinion in the fixed arm just meshes correctly, allowing just a trifle for end-shake. The pinion, of course, should revolve quite freely in the window of the fixed arm.

Now follows the second contrate wheel and striking barrel. This is shown in Fig. 22, Nos. 9, 9a, 9b and 9c. The contrate wheel is the same as that attached to the chime barrel, except that the spigot at the back of the wheel has a total length

Chiming and striking barrels and fixed arm

of 3/8 in. Fitting the outside diameter of the spigot are the two discs. To the larger disc, which is 1 1/2 in. dia., the contrate wheel is screwed with three equidistant 10 B.A. screws. This disc has five equidistant notches filed in its rim, but this should not be done at the moment.

Then comes the smaller disc, 1 1/4 in. dia. This disc in turn is screwed by three equidistant 10 B.A. screws to the larger disc, but short circular slots are filed in the smaller disc so that when the large mushroom-headed 10 B.A. screws have been

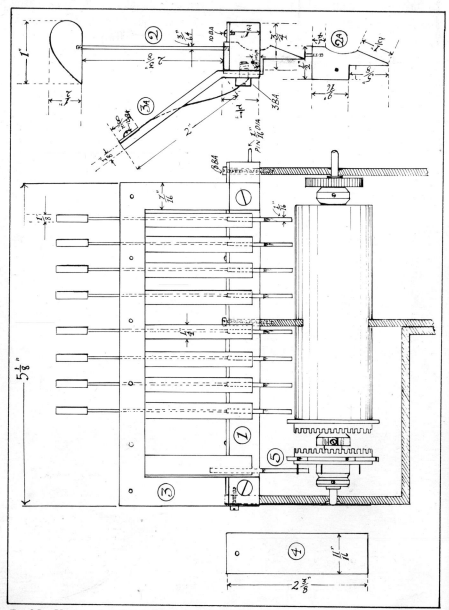

Fig.25   Various details of chiming and striking train

fitted, the smaller disc can be rotated slightly for adjustment purposes.

There are five equidistant lifting pins 1/32 in. dia., fitted at right angles to the side of this disc at 1/8 in. distance from the outer edge of the disc. The spigot or boss of the contrate wheel is bored to be a nice running fit on the chime barrel arbor.

The left-hand end of the phosphor-bronze bush previously fitted to the fixed arm is turned to such a length that the striking contrate wheel meshes correctly with the pinion in the window of the fixed arm.

Finally, another phosphor-bronze set collar and binding screw are made and fitted to the chime barrel arbor to keep the contrate wheel in mesh with the pinion of the fixed arm. This assembly cannot quite be finally finished until the pins are placed in the chiming barrel, and this procedure is about the final operation before the movement can be considered finished.

The complete train should now be pivoted and, as previously stated, it is better to lay the wheels and pinions between the inside edges of the movement plates so that the correct positions for the pivots can be obtained. They are all turned and finished in exactly the same way as the time train.

After pivoting the train, it should be run in the movement frame; in Fig. 23 will be seen the approximate positions of the wheels and pinions. Their correct positions must of course be obtained with the depth tool. The front pivot of the chime barrel arbor has its pivot hole made in this front movement plate in a similar way to the other pivots, but its back pivot runs in a cock screwed to the back movement plate.

This cock is shown in Figs. 24, 25 and again in Fig. 26, which gives the dimensions. The outer edge of the side of the cock is in line with the edge of the side of the back movement plate. The upper arm of the cock is steadied with a No. 8 B.A. screw, screwed into the end of the chime hammer rack. The lower arm of the cock is screwed to the back movement plate with two 2 B.A. screws, and two steady pins are also fitted.

The back movement plate has an arc cut out of it to allow the chime barrel to pass through. The diameter of this arc is approximately 1 1/2 in. After marking out the arc and before cutting the plate, the chime barrel pivot hole should be drilled, using the pivot hole in the front movement plate as a guide.

If a piece of steel rod of suitable diameter, with one end turned to a point, is passed through both holes in the movement plate it will be easy to get the position

Chiming and striking barrel

Chiming and striking train with barrels in position

of the back pivot hole in the correct position in the cock. Afterwards, the arc in the back movement plate should be cut out with a fretsaw, followed by fine filing and finishing with buff sticks. Before commencing the front plate mechanism, the musical train should be made and run in the movement plates.

Musical train

Fig. 27 shows the musical train except the fly and musical barrel. Fig. 27, No. 1, shows the barrel and great wheel, both of which are the same in all respects as the chiming and striking great wheel and barrel, so no further description is necessary.

Nos. 2 and 2a give details of the second wheel and pinion. The wheel is cut with a 40 dp cutter and contains 80 teeth. The full diameter is 1 in., the pinion head has nine leaves, and is Q gauge drill size. There may be some difficulty in getting this pinion wire with nine leaves. The writer cut his pinion, but it is suggested that an eight-leaved pinion be used instead.

If using an eight leaf-pinion, the diameter would be approximately L gauge drill

Chiming and striking train with barrels removed

size. Substituting the eight-leaf pinion for a nine-leaf will make no difference to the layout of the wheels; it will only bring the pivot of the second wheel arbor slightly nearer the pivot of the great arbor. The driving weight will not descend quite so rapidly, but this would allow of the musical train being let off occasionally by tripping the let-off lever by hand.

It will be seen that the back pivot of the second arbor is extended and projects from the back movement plate. This extension carries the locking-plate disc, the purpose of which will be explained later. Nos. 3 and 3a represent the cam wheel. This is cut with the 40 dp cutter and contains 64 teeth, the diameter being 1 11/16 in. The pinion has eight leaves and is in diameter B gauge drill size.

The drawing of this cam explains itself. It is approximately 1/32 in. thick. It will be seen that there is a small distance piece between the face of the wheel and the face of the cam. The distance piece is riveted to the cam as a fixture, and a small screw holds the cam and distance piece to the wheel. Nos. 4 and 4a show the two idle wheels that connect the musical barrel which, with the second wheel of the

57

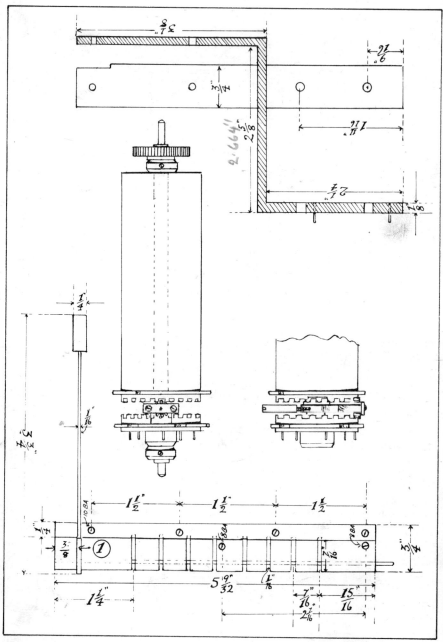

Fig. 26 Details of chiming and striking barrels, hammer rack and large cock

train, these two wheels are identical with in every way. Their arbor should be made from silver steel.

Nos. 5 and 5a show the warning wheel and pinion. From the drawing it will be seen that the wheel is a contrate one, and it is cut in a similar way to the contrate

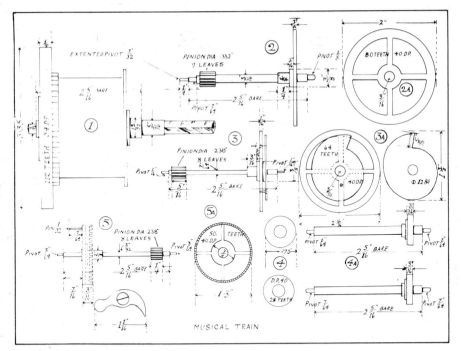

Fig. 27 Working drawings of musical train

wheels of the chiming barrel. The wheel contains 50 teeth, and is cut with the 40 dp cutter. The rim of the wheel near the tops of the teeth should not be more than 3/64 in. thick. This wheel must be very carefully mounted on its collet, so that the teeth run true in plane as well as concentrically.

The pinion head has eight leaves and its diameter is B gauge drill size. Note there is a pin in this wheel for locking purposes.

CHAPTER EIGHT

The vertical fly and the musical barrel

We now come to details of the vertical fly and the musical barrel.

Fig. 28, Nos. 1, 1a, 1b and 1c give the details of the vertical fly. A vertical fly runs more easily and is quieter than a horizontal fly, so it is more suitable for a musical train.

It is constructed in a similar way to the chime fly, but the dimensions are somewhat different. The pinion head is B gauge drill size, or 15/64 in. dia., and it has eight leaves. Nos. 2 and 2a show the upper cock or bracket of the fly, which is positioned and screwed to the outside of the back movement plate.

There is a small end-plate of hardened steel screwed to the under side of the cock on which the end of the lower pivot of the fly arbor revolves.

The musical barrel

Fig. 28, Nos. 3, 3a and 3b give the details of the musical barrel and its gearwheel. This wheel is 1/2 in. wide and is the same diameter as the second wheel of the train and contains the same number of teeth, being cut with the 40 dp cutter in order to lighten its weight. A recess or sink is turned from its outer side. This recess is indicated in No. 3b, shown in dotted lines in the drawing.

The chime barrel arbor is made from a length of silver steel 1/4 in. dia., and has

Chiming and striking barrels, fly and fly cock

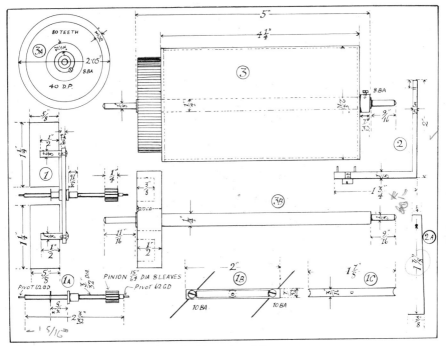

Fig. 28 Working drawings of musical barrel and fly

the chime wheel fixed to it by way of a collet, but instead of riveting it to the collet it is a nice push fit, retained in place by a small screw in the junction of the wheel and collet. This can be seen in 3a.

The musical barrel itself is built up from a length of 2 5/16 in. dia. brass tube and has circular brass discs soldered to each end of the tube. It is preferable, though not essential, to turn a small recess in the thickness of the wall at the ends of the tube or the brass discs to bed against, and a three-point steady in the lathe fitment to use for this operation.

The two discs must not be an absolutely tight fit. Room must be left for the soft solder. A good way to do the soldering is to flux and position the disc in the end of the tube and stand the latter on end and place three small pieces of solder at the appropriate positions, then heat up the tube with the bunsen burner held in the hand.

A good general heat applied near the business end of the tube will cause the solder to flow around like water. The holes in the centre of the discs can be bored before soldering. It should be noted that one disc has a set collar fixed to it. It is riveted to the disc before the soldering operation.

Next a turning mandrel should be prepared. A length of 1/4 in. dia. silver-steel rod is centred at each end and the barrel is now clamped to the mandrel by the binding screw in the set collar. The barrel is turned true all over between lathe centres. Light cuts with a knife tool will be necessary for this procedure, as the brass tube will have a tendency to chatter. It took the writer three hours to turn down the tube true and polish it!

61

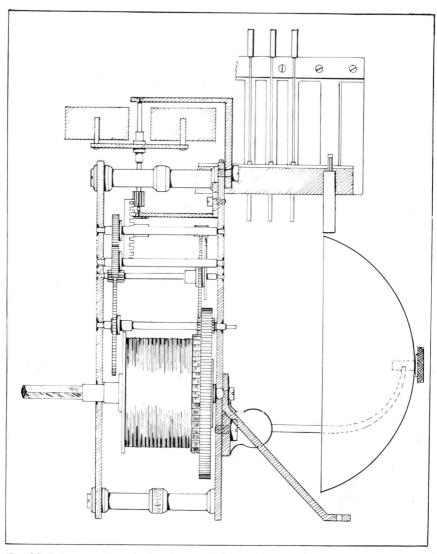

Fig. 29 Side view of musical train, musical barrel removed

The barrel is a push fit on its arbor and is not fixed by any screws to the chime gearwheel; it is clamped to the arbor by the binding screw in the set collar attached to the disc at the end of the barrel. The reason for this will be explained later. This then completes the musical train, which should now be pivoted and run on the movement plates.

To get the depthing correct between the contrate warning wheel and the fly pinion may appear a bit of a problem. But if the bottom cock or bracket that carries the pivot of the fly arbor is clamped temporarily to the inside of the back movement plate, the position of the pivot hole can be roughly estimated by eye, and should be marked a little too much in mesh.

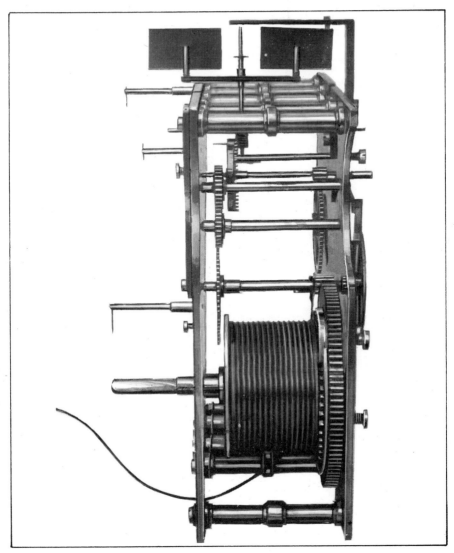

Musical train, musical barrel removed

After drilling the pivot hole the back of the cock that fits against the back movement plate can be reduced by filing. If this is done gradually, a perfect depth will be the result. It will then be easy to get the position of the upper pivot of the fly with the top cock by measuring off from the lower pivot hole. The fly arbor must have a little endplay.

Fig. 29 shows a side view of the musical train between the plates, but the musical barrel is not in position. The hammer rack shown broken in the drawing belongs to the chiming train. It is depicted here to show the relative position of the hour hammer and the large hour bell.

Fig. 30 is the same view with the musical barrel in position. This drawing also

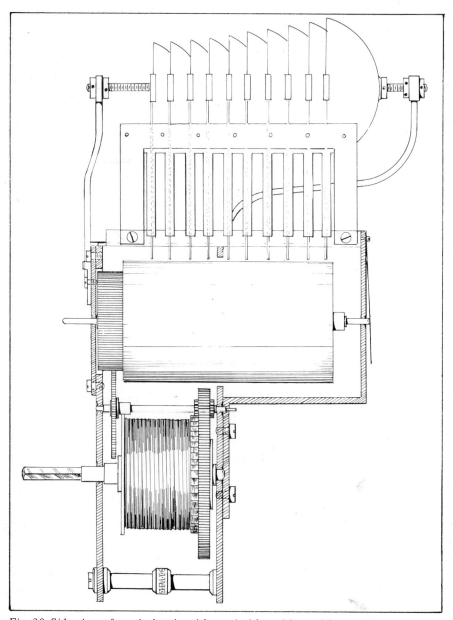

Fig. 30 Side view of musical train with musical barrel in position

shows the musical hammer frame in position.

Fig. 31 shows a front view of the musical train. It should be noted that the second wheel of the train drives the cam-wheel pinion and also the first idler. This idler drives the second idler, which in turn drives the gearwheel of the musical barrel arbor.

In Fig. 31 will be seen details of the bottom cock of the vertical fly. When

Musical train, musical barrel in position

finally fitted, it should be screwed and steady-pinned to the back movement plate. The front pivot of the musical barrel arbor runs in a vertical brass strip attached to the front plate. When finally fitted it should be screwed and steady-pinned to the front movement plate. The back pivot of the musical barrel arbor runs in a large cock which is screwed and steady-pinned to the back movement plate in a similar way as the chime barrel arbor.

Details of the brass strip and the cock are given in Fig. 32, Nos. 1 and 1a for the former, and Nos. 2 and 2a for the latter. The cock should be built up and the joints silver soldered to make a strong job. No. 3 is a steel spring, the upper end of which is screwed to the top of the cock. Its purpose is to keep the back pivot of the barrel arbor pumped in the direction of the front movement plate.

There is a lever on the front movement plate which controls the position of the pivots of the arbor, and with it the musical barrel itself between distance apart of

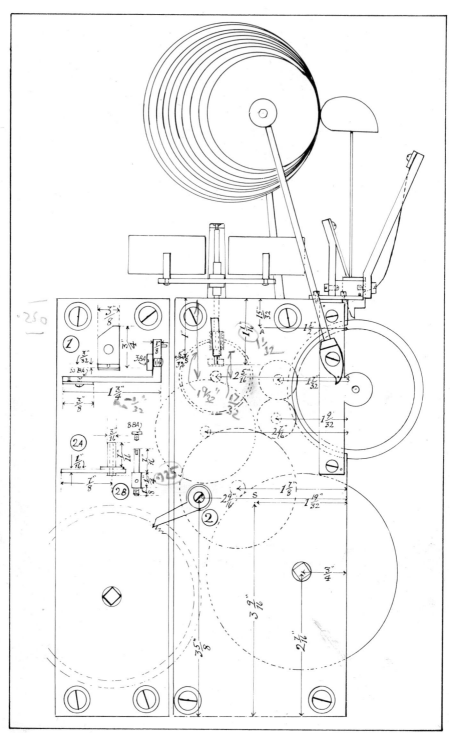

Fig. 31 Front view of musical train

the two movement plates. This movement of the barrel is required for the changing of the tune to be played, and will be explained later.

About half the width of the cock is proud of the side of the back movement plate. This is shown clearly in Fig. 32a, which shows the complete view of the back of the movement. This concludes all the internal work of the movement, except the maintaining click.

This item is seen in Fig. 31, No. 2 in position. The point of the tip of click is in one of the maintaining ratchet wheel teeth. Its stud is screwed to the inner surface of the back movement plate, and Nos. 2a and 2b give details of its construction.

There remains the two hammer racks to make, and also the various levers and other parts situated on the outside of the movement plates.

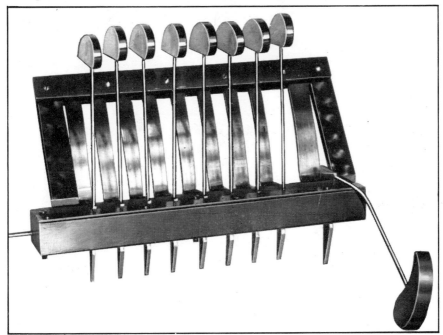

Hammer rack and springs of chiming and striking train

Fig. 25, No. 1 shows the Chiming hammer rack in position on the movement frame, and No. 2 gives details of dimensions. A plan view from above is also shown in Fig. 26, No. 1.

The rack itself is made from a piece of brass 3/4 in. wide x 1/2 in. high, and approximately 5 9/32 in. in length. The first thing to do is to produce a small hole, say 1/16 in. dia., from end to end in the brass block. This hole accommodates a long pin which locks all the hammers in their respective slots.

The way to make this hole is to mill a long groove from one end of the block to the other. A small circular saw does this very well. If there is no means of milling this in the lathe, it can be accomplished with a hacksaw instead. Next, a strip of brass is then filed to fit in this groove but before soft soldering the strip in position, the long pin should be greased and put in position in the bottom of the groove. The strip of brass is then placed in position and fluxed.

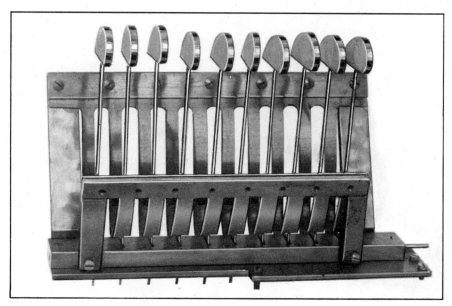

Hammer rack and springs of musical train

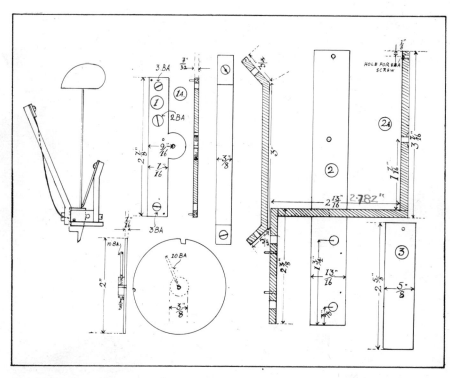

Fig. 32 Various details of musical train

Lay the block on a brick and heat up well with the bunsen burner. The solder must be made to flow from end to end of the brass strip, and also on both sides of the strip. Before the solder cools off, the pin should be kept moving in case any solder has leaked through the bottom edge of the strip and soldered the pin to the groove.

After this operation, the block should be thoroughly washed in ammonia and water and well dried over the bunsen burner.

Now mark the positions of the slots that the hammers function in. The width of the slots is 1/16 in. The slots are best cut with a circular saw of this width, either in the lathe or milling machine if available. However, if this is not possible the slots can be cut with a hack saw and finished with a file of suitable width.

As it is almost impossible to file absolutely flat, it is advisable to place the block

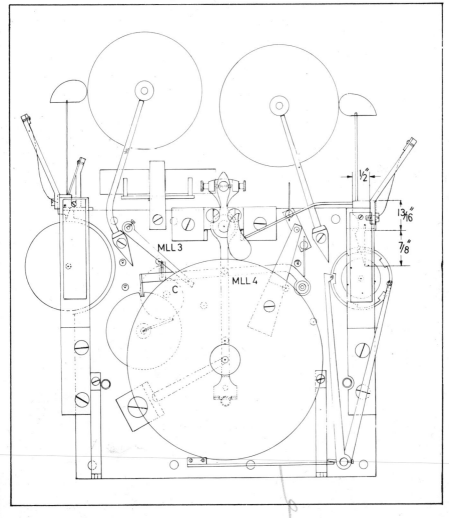

Fig. 32a View of back of movement

between two pieces of wood which have previously been slotted. By this means the file will be kept from wobbling. It is most important that the sides of the slots are produced true and flat, otherwise when it comes to fitting the steel hammers they will wobble when being moved by the pins in the barrel.

The slots are cut about 7/16 in. deep and it will be seen in Fig. 25, No. 2 that there is a strip of thin metal (it can be either brass or steel) screwed to the top of the block. The front edges of the hammers butt against this strip after they have been released by the pins on the barrel.

As this strip covers part of the length of the slots, the hammers can swing backwards but are checked by the strip when they reach their normal resting postion. The hammer shown in the extreme left hand slot (Fig. 26, No. 1) represents the hour hammer as viewed from above. This hammer is again seen in Figs. 25 and 32a.

Making the hammers

The next thing to do is to make the eight chiming hammers and the hour hammer. A side view of the former is shown in Fig. 25, Nos. 2 and 2a. The parts that work in the hammer rack are made from mild-steel plate 1/16 in. thick.

They should be cut out with a fretsaw and after the hole for the pin has been drilled they should all be assembled on a spare piece of pin and clamped in the vice and all their respective edges filed up together. This will ensure their being of equal dimensions. They should now be finished with emery sticks.

The top edge of each hammer is drilled and tapped 12 B.A. This requires care to avoid breaking through the thickness of the hammer with the drill.

Procure some mild-steel wire, about 12 B.A. diameter, and cut the eight hammer stems. A 12 B.A. thread is cut at each end. One end should be firmly screwed into the previously tapped hole, taking care not to break the stem off.

The hammer heads are made from 1/8 in. brass plate. They are cut out with the fretsaw and will require fine finishing and polishing. They are drilled and tapped 12 B.A. and screwed on to the other end of the hammer stems.

CHAPTER NINE

The musical hammers

The plate and hammer springs and the musical hammers are among the items now described.

The back view of the plate with the hammer springs is shown in Fig. 25, Nos. 3 and 3a. The plate or frame consists of brass of 1/8 in. thickness x about 7/16 in. in width. I mitred the brass strip at the corners and afterwards silver soldered the joints. If preferred, it can be cut out of a large piece of 1/8 in. thick brass plate.

The frame should be filed up and finished, and when it is ready to be attached to the back of the hammer block—the sides of the frame are partially cut through and bent at an angle as shown in 3a—it can be cut through with a file; and after closing the joint it should be either soft soldered or hard soldered.

The brass springs for the hammers are made from a piece of shim brass which should be carefully flattened. This can easily be done by laying it on a flat surface and stroking the curved surface with the edge of a flat ruler. After marking out the dimensions it should be cut with a very fine fretsaw blade.

The free ends of the spring should not be cut through until all the sides have first been cut. Shim brass of 15 thou. is a suitable thickness for the springs. Fig. 25, No. 3a shows how the springs are fixed to the frame. It will be seen that they are sandwiched between the top member of the frame and a 1/16 in. thick brass strip secured with No. 10 B.A. screws put through the strip and the shim and screwed into the thickness of the top member of the frame. The frame is then fixed to the back of the brass block with two No. 3 B.A. screws. Care must be taken in placing these screws so that they do not foul the retaining pin of the hammers.

Positioning the hammer frame

The hammer springs should be bent so that the free ends make pressure on the back of the hammers at a point only just above the centre line of the hammer-retaining pin. It should be emphasised that an absolute minimum spring pressure is all that is required otherwise the available driving power of the weight will be insufficient for the pins in the chime barrel fully to lift the hammers.

Referring to Fig. 23 it will be seen that a right-angled section has been cut away from the top and sides of both movement plates. This section is the same length as the width of the block, but its height is a trifle longer than that of the block. The position of the hammer frame should be so arranged that the ends of the tails of the hammers are in line with the pivot centres of the chime arbor—or preferably slightly past the centres, but not before centres as it seems to appear in the drawing.

The hammer tails should just be clear of the surface of the chime barrel. This can be arranged when cutting the section in the movement plates. It will be found easier to finish filing both sections with the frame assembled.

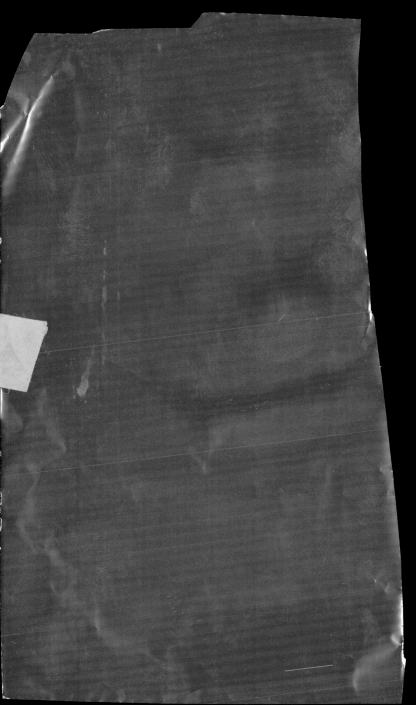

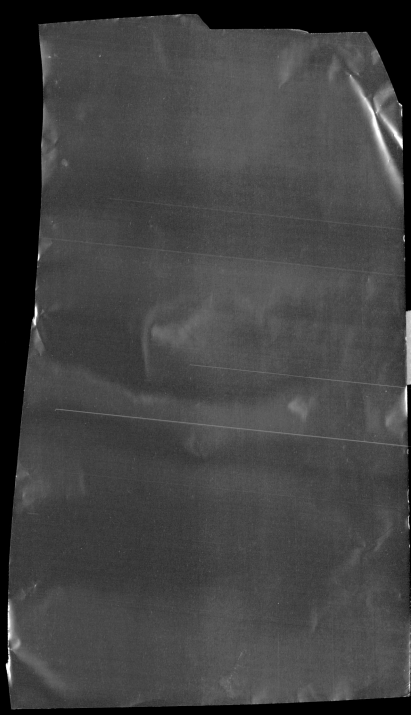

5/16" THICK GAUGE PLATE

5 1/8" LONG —   1 6/ 1 3/16"

1 6/ 1 5/16"

For VICE JAWS

The hammer frame or rack should now be fitted and screwed to the movement frame. It is held to the latter by two No. 8 B.A. screws passing right through the thickness of the block into the thickness of the movement plates. A good way to obtain the position for drilling the holes for the screws is to hold or clamp the frame in position on the movement frame and then, with a fine steel point, scribe very carefully on the under side of the block the position of the edges of the plates of the movement frame.

Now find the centre distance between the scribed lines and at a suitable spot (about midway of the width of the block) centre pop a small dot, then drill the hole from the under side of the block. Next reassemble the block on the movement frame. Using the scribed lines as a guide, insert a drill in the hole upside down, and a light tap on the cutting end of the drill with the wooden handle of the hammer will produce a centre pop for drilling the hole in the plates.

It is very important that the hole be dead central with the thickness of the plates as the diameter of a No. 8 B.A. fixing screw will occupy most of the thickness of the plate. It is awkward to drill these holes in the drilling machine owing to the height of the plates. The only alternative is to do the drilling with a hand drill; if a very short drill is used it can be accomplished quite successfully. Two long No. 8 B.A. screws will have to be made—and just a short length of thread on each screw is all that is needed.

Care must be taken—when the chime arbor is in position in the frame—that the shoulder of the front pivot is against the inside front movement plate, and that the

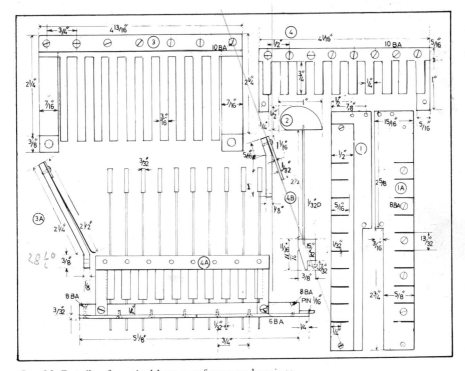

Fig. 33 Details of musical hammer frame and springs

View showing musical side of movement

last-chime hammer does not foul the side of the disc at the end of the chime barrel. A reference again to Fig. 25 will show what is required.

The left-hand end of the hammer block is cut to such a length that the upper arm of the large cock that holds the back pivot of the chime arbor just meets the end of the hammer block to which it is held by a No. 8 B.A. screw. This same screw holds a thin steel spring, the lower end of which is always in contact with the end of the pivot of the chime arbor and keeps this item always pumped towards the front movement plate. This spring is shown in position in Fig. 25 and No. 4 shows the face view of it.

The four hammer shown at the extreme left-hand end of the block is made a little heavier than the chime hammers. Its tail is also longer. The exact length is better obtained by trial after the five lifting pins have been inserted in the striking barrel. It must be remembered that when the striking barrel is at rest the tail of the

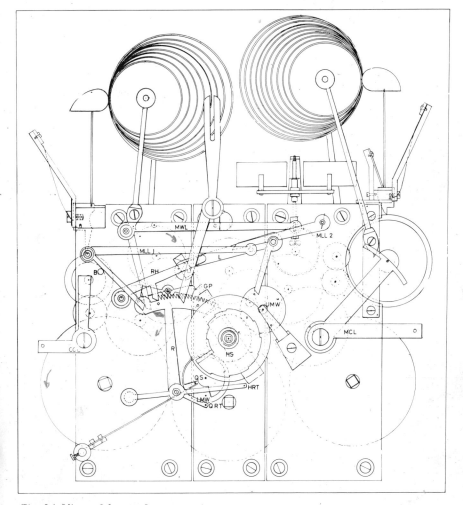

Fig. 34 View of front of movement

hour hammer will be midway between two adjacent lifting pins. Fig. 25, No. 5 shows the back view of the steel portion of the hour striking hammer that works in the block. Fig. 26 shows the plan view of the hour hammer from above and Fig. 29 shows another view of the hammer and its relative position with the large bell.

This bell, which is about 5 in. in diameter, is held by a standard screwed to the back-movement plate. This standard is built up from angle brass and its stem is silver soldered into the angle brass; and a knurled nut holds the bell in position on the upper end of the standard. It is made in a similar way to the bell standards used always in French clocks. It should be screwed and steady pinned to the back movement plate, using a No. 0 B.A. screw with a large head. Such a screw has to be made.

The musical hammer frame is constructed on rather different lines from that of the chiming hammer frame. First, there is a brass baseplate 3/32 in. in thickness and approximately 5 3/8 in. in total length. This is shown in Fig. 33. No. 1 shows the baseplate from above with the block proper in position. No. 1a shows the plan view from below. It will be noticed that a section of slightly more than half the length of the baseplate has been cut away.

The block proper consists of a length of brass 1/2 in. in width by 5 5/8 in. inn length, its height being 1/4 in. It is screwed with No. 8 B.A. countersunk screws in the extreme ends to the base, and four similar screws are screwed from the under side of the baseplate into the block proper. Previous to screwing these two items together, a groove 1/16 in. sq. is milled from end to end in the under side of the block proper. This groove is to accommodate the retaining pin for the 10 hammers and the slots for these should next be cut, their distance apart being approximately 13/32 in. They are cut 5/16 in. deep x 1/32 in. in width and are produced in a similar way to the slots in the chime-hammer frame.

The 10 musical hammers

Fig. 33, No. 2 represents the musical hammers. They are similar to the chime-quarter hammers. The flat portions that work in the slots are cut from 1/32 in. thickness steel plate. The hammer stems are about 1/32 in. in diameter and are not threaded and tapped into the flat steel portion of the hammer; but a small slot is filed in the latter just to fit the diameter of the stems which are then silver soldered in position, afterwards being smoothed off.

The hammer heads are the same size as the chime-quarter hammer heads, but only 3/32 in. in thickness. They can either be drilled and tapped to screw on the stems or drilled and soft soldered to the stems.

Levers of front plate mechanism

The construction of the plate and hammer springs is similar to its chime contemporary, only the dimensions being different. Fig. 33, Nos. 3 and 3a shows all the details that are required.

The buffer springs

Instead of having a fixed stop for the hammers to butt against, a set of 10 buffer springs or flexible stops is provided for the hammers. The frame for this component is shown in Fig. 33, Nos. 4, 4a and 4b. The actual springs are cut out of one piece of brass plate 1/32 in. in thickness, which is screwed to the plate in a similar way to the springs on the other plate. From the drawing it will be seen that it is screwed to the front of the hammer block with two No. 6 B.A. screws. Care must be taken not to run the screws into the sides of the slots.

The complete hammer frame should now be mounted on the movement frame. In this case no cutting of the plates is necessary, Figs. 30, 31, 32 and 34 show the hammer frame mounted in position on the movement plates. The hammer tails should be in the line with the pivot centres of the musical barrel, and the tips of the tails should just clear the surface of the musical barrel.

Two No. 8 B.A. screws are used for fixing this fitment to the front movement plate. It is further secured by another No. 8 B.A. screw put through the large musical-barrel cock into the end of the hammer frame. This last screw also retains in position the thin steel spring for controlling the end-shake of the musical barrel pivots when the left-hand pivot shoulder of the musical barrel is against the brass strip screwed to the front movement plate.

The last hammer (No. 10) should be approximately 1/16 in. from the back rim of the musical barrel. This is clearly shown in Fig. 30. A change tune lever will be described later for pumping the musical barrel backwards for changing the tunes.

As in the case of the chime barrel it is better to defer pinning the musical barrel until the front and back plate mechanism has been made.

The bells

The two sets of bells can, however, be mounted. (The sets can be obtained from Messrs Mears and Stainbank, 114 Whitechapel Road, London, E.C.). The cost of a set of bells varies in relation to the size and number in the set, but is quite moderate and excellent value. They are already tuned and only require mounting.

The usual method of mounting them is on a steel rod with wooden distance washers between each bell. The end of the rod is threaded, a nut fitted and then they are tightened up. But an objection to this plan is that the pressure of the distance washers kills quite an amount of their sounding power.

A method I have adopted is to tap a thread in the hole of each bell and screw them on a length of threaded studding. By this method the bells are supported quite loosely—as they should be to get the best possible results—and, moreover, they can be turned round to get the best position for the hammers to strike them. No working drawings are shown of the bell standards, but in the various drawings will be seen what is required.

Formerly steel forgings were obtainable for these items, but it required an enormous amount of labour to finish them well. The spoon-shaped piece is cut

77

from 3/16 in thickness brass. A hole should then be drilled in the flat top-end of the spoon and the end of a suitable size piece of round brass rod is fitted to the hole, followed by silver soldering the two together. This makes a perfect joint with the minimum amount of finishing to do afterwards.

To the other end of the rod is fitted a disc of brass of the same thickness as the spoon. This is also silver soldered to the brass rod. A 3/16 in. clearance hole is drilled through the disc and then two ring nuts are made and fitted for clamping the threaded rod to the bell standard.

It will be noted that the hammer heads are all in line with one another and the bells are arranged in a staggered position. This is better practice than mounting the bells square with the movement frame and bending the hammer stems for the hammer heads to reach the smaller diameter bells; by adopting this method the chiming tends to be uneven when in action.

Before making the front and back plate letting-off mechanism the action should be carefully studied and thoroughly understood, as the functioning of the chiming, striking and musical playing are entirely dependent on these parts working properly.

Fig. 34 shows a complete view of the front-plate mechanism with the various levers returned to their normal resting position just after three o'clock has been chimed, struck and one tune played. The names of the various levers are referred to by letters and these letters are shown in the drawing.

It will be assumed that the minute hand is approaching the hour of three o'clock. One of the four lifting pins in the upper-minute wheel referred to as UMW will be approaching the lower arm of the lifter referred to as L and will gradually raise the lifter. Positioned at the left-hand end of the upper arm of the lifter is a pin which will raise the rack hook referred to as RH.

As the rack hook is gradually raised the point of the hook will be drawn away from the first tooth of the rack referred to as R. At the moment this happens the rack will fall and the pin in the long tail of the rack referred to as HRT will fall against the third highest step of the hour snail referred to as HS and at the same time as this happens the chiming warning wheel (centred near MLL 1) will rotate a short distance until the pin in its rim is arrested by the stop block fixed on the inside upper arm of the lifter.

This stop block goes through a slot cut in the left-hand movement plate. The lifting pin meanwhile on the upper-minute wheel will continue to raise—slightly—the stop block until finally the pin in the upper minute wheel will move past the extremity of the lower arm of the lifter, with the result that the rack hook will drop its point into the seventh tooth from the left-hand end of the rack.

A total of seven teeth are required ffr chiming and striking the hour of three o'clock; four for the four peals of the chime and three for the striking of the hour, when the rack falls. The quarter rack tail, referred to as QRT, will not reach what would be the fourth step on the quarter snail, as this has been cut away. The quarter snail is superimposed on the lower-minute wheel.

As soon as the rack hook has fallen into the seventh tooth of the rack the gathering pallet, referred to as GP, will rotate and gather up each of the seven teeth of the rack and, as the last tooth is gathered, one of the wings of the gathering pallet will be locked by the pin in the back of the rack.

78

The change-over from chime to strike

Looking at Fig. 34 at the bottom left-hand front movement plate will be seen a long thin spring. This spring is clamped to the extremity of an arbor that passes through both movement plates, and shortly before the hour is chimed and struck a pin situated in the face of the lower-minute wheel impels the free end of this spring downwards, causing the arbor to rotate slightly clockwise.

Now at the bottom right-hand corner of Fig. 32a will be seen the other end of the arbor, to the extremity of which is clamped a two-arm lever, with a pin fixed on the upper end of each arm. The pin in the left-hand arm will have fallen into one of the five notches around the circumference of the brass disc situated at the left-hand end of the chime barrel arbor.

So long as the pin remains in its notch in the disc no rotation of the striking barrel can occur. Meanwhile the pin in the right-hand upper arm will be resting against the circumference of the disc attached to the end of the chime barrel. At the completion of the fourth peal of the chime the pin will enter the notch in the chime barrel disc and, at the same time, the pin will come out of the notch on the disc of the striking barrel, which will at once rotate—with the result that three o'clock will be struck on the large hour bell.

The two-arm lever will remain in its present position until about three minutes past the hour when the path of the pin in the lower minute wheel will be moved away from the extremity of the long spring, which will at once resume its normal position. This is due to the fact that situated at the bottom of the back movement plate is a weak counterspring which will return the two-arm lever to its previous position.

The pin in the left-hand arm will enter one of the five notches of the disc attached to the striking barrel and thus lock it. At the same time the pin in the upper end of the right arm will come out of the disc attached to the chime barrel and thus leave the chime barrel free for the next quarter. When about to chime the quarter past the hour, the highest step in the quarter snail on the lower-minute wheel will be in the correct position for the pin in the end of the shorter rack tail to fall against it—and thus the rack will only fall one tooth. The longer rack tail will not reach the hour snail situated on the hour socket tube.

The action at the half hour is the same except that the second step of the quarter snail is presented to the pin in the end of the short rack tail. As the third quarter the same action takes place, but in this case it is the third step of the quarter snail that is presented to the pin in the short rack tail.

It is only at the hour that the fourth step of the quarter snail is not used and, as previously stated, this segment of the snail is cut away so that the pin in the short rack tail cannot reach it, but does allow the pin in the long-rack tail to contact the steps of the hour snail when the rack falls.

The musical release mechanism

The musical train is arrested by the long arm of the cam on the cam wheel looking against the stop block attached to the musical-locking lever referred to as C and MLL 4; on drawings this is shown in Fig. 32a. It is situated on the back movement plate and its pivot centre is seen near the chiming fly cock. The stop block is riveted to the lever near the left-hand end and goes through a slot cut out of the back movement plate.

Now going back to Fig. 34, there will be seen towards the top of the front movement plate a long two-arm lever which is the musical-locking lever, and referred to as MLL 1. There is a pin in the right-hand end of the long arm of the lever which will lift another arm of a shorter lever. The right end of this arm is cross-pinned to an arbor which goes through both movement plates. This lever is referred to as MLL 2.

Situated on the extremity of the pivot to this arbor that passes through the back movement plate (Fig. 32a) will be seen another lever, referred to as MLL 3. The upper end of the lever is clamped to the pivot by a binding screw, but the lower end of the lever has a pin which will raise the cam-locking lever and release the musical train.

CHAPTER TEN

The chiming sequence

Continuing our examination of the chiming sequence if we look again at the cam locking lever, it will be noted that at the extreme left-hand end there is a hook whose point is resting in a notch on the circumference of a disc known as the locking plate.

So long as the point of the hook is in the notch of the locking plate the musical train will be locked, but when the point of the hook is out of the notch and resting on the circumference of the locking plate the musical train will run subject to the warning wheel not being locked, which will be explained later.

The locking plate does not of itself arrest the train, but controls the position of the cam locking lever. The locking plate is clamped on to the extended pivot of the second wheel of the musical train.

Referring again to Fig. 34, there will be seen a long two-arm lever nearest to the top of the front movement plate. This is the musical warning lever, referred to as MWL. Every time the rack falls, the right-hand end of the long arm of the lever will also fall and with it a stop block which is attached to it and passes through a slot cut in the right-hand front movement plate.

When in the down position the stop block is ready to arrest the rotation of the musical warning wheel by intercepting a pin placed in the rim of the warning wheel. But as the musical train is only released at the hour, it is returned again to its usual resting position by the same pin on the under side of the rack that locks the wing of the gathering pallet.

Looking at Fig. 34 again, it will be noticed that the lower arm of the musical locking lever No. 1 is resting against a banking pin situated on the left-hand front movement plate, referred to as B. There is a pin in the front face of the rack near the first tooth which is so placed that when the rack falls at the first, second and third quarters, this pin will not quite reach the upper edge of the lower arm of the lever MLL 1, but at the hour the rack will fall further to the left, and in falling the pin in the rack will push past lever MLL 1 and arrive at the under side of the arm of lever MLL 1.

As the rack is gathered up, this pin will raise the lower arm of MLL 1 which in turn will raise MLL 2, MLL 3 and finally the cam-locking lever, MLL 4. The musical train will at once run until the pin in the warning wheel is arrested by the stop block of the musical warning lever.

This lever having fallen when the rack fell, the musical train will thus remain locked during the chiming and striking until the last tooth of the rack is finally gathered up, when the pin in the under side of the rack will contact the lower arm of the musical warning lever and raise it, and with it the long upper arm, to normal resting position. As soon as this happens, the musical train will run and play its tune.

Front view of movement, showing position of various levers

This is a long explanation, but it is given in full in order to make the various actions clear.

The change chime lever is shown on the front left-hand movement plate in a midway position near the left-hand edge of the plate, and referred to as CCL. This is a simple affair. Its upper arm is partially bevelled off, and its function is to pump the chime barrel arbor endways to bring another set of pins in line with the tails of the chime hammer.

The change tune lever is shown and situated on the front right-hand movement plate, referred to as MCL, and it functions the same way as the change chime lever. Referring again to Fig. 34, it will be noted there is a two-arm lever at the top of the centre movement plate. This is used for silencing the chimes, strike and music.

There is a chime silent dial and hand situated in the arch of the dial plate, which

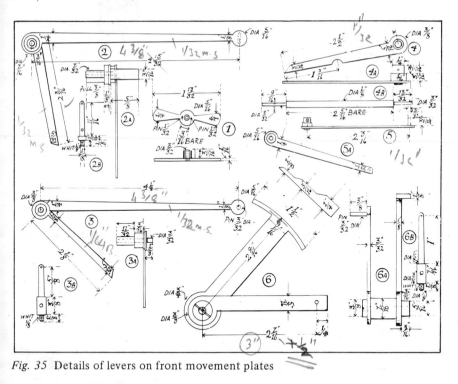

Fig. 35 Details of levers on front movement plates

controls this lever. When this hand points to the silent position the lower arm of the lever will prevent the rack falling by contacting a pin fitted in the front fall of the rack. This pin is situated towards the right hand end of the rack.

Construction of the various levers

Fig. 35, No. 1. The gathering pallet. Make the hub from a short length of 3/32 in. mild-steel rod which is riveted from the under side to the flat winged part of the pallet.

Drill centrally a small hole in the rod. Next a broken piece of a square needle file is gently hammered into the hole and driven out again. This process is continued until a nice internal square has been formed. It must fit the square on the front pivot of the pallet wheel arbor in all four positions.

When finally riveted to the winged part of the pallet, the under side of the latter should be at a distance of about 5/32 in. from the front movement plate. The drawing gives the dimensions required. The finishing of the extremities of the wings to length are better left until the rack has been made.

To lock the gathering pallet to the square of the pallet, first a very small hole is drilled in the latter and a cross pin fitted. As an alternative the end of the square can be threaded and a minute square nut made and fitted.

The writer prefers this way, although not often seen. Two pins of 1/32 in. dia. are fitted to the winged part of the pallet diametrically opposite each other, their centres apart being approximately 3/16 in. These pins do the gathering up of the rack.

The rack

Fig. 36, No. 1. The rack is cut from a piece of 1/32 in. or 3/64 in. thick mild-steel plate. A centre pop is made for the position of the rack hub centre, and an arc scribed from this centre with a radius of 2 15/32 in., which will represent the distance from the tips of the teeth to the rack centre.

If possible, the points of the rack teeth should be cut with a fine slotting saw in the lathe. This can be arranged by mounting a 4 1/2 in. dia. wood disc on the face or catchplate of the lathe, and clamping the blank rack in position on the wood disc. Bring up the tailstock centre to the popped hole in the rack and clamp the rack to the disc with a number of drawing pins inserted at convenient positions.

The segment at the top of the rack can now be turned by a sharp knife tool, by partially rotating the lathe mandrel by hand. It is difficult to state the pitch distance between each tooth, but the distance from the first tooth to the last or nineteenth should not exceed 1 1/2 in.; slightly less would be better; if a division plate with a 192-hole circle or thereabouts is available, this will give the pitch distance of the teeth. The teeth should be slit through, and the depth of the cut is a full 3/32 in.

Now demount the rack from the faceplate and cut the backs of the teeth by hand with a fine fretsaw, taking care not to encroach into the cut made by the slitting saw. Follow this by filing the backs of the teeth with a small half-round needle file to form a nice curve to the backs of the teeth. This is necessary to allow enough room for the pins of the gathering pallet to function without catching on the backs of the teeth.

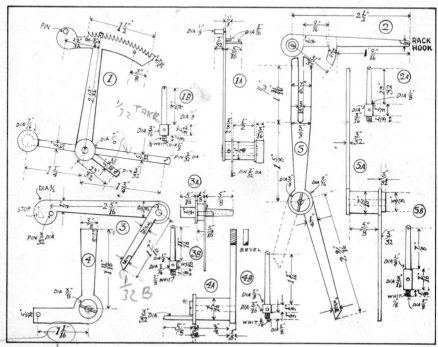

Fig. 36 Details of levers on front movement plates

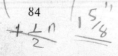

The rest of the rack should now be cut to shape and nicely finished off. A 1/16 in. dia. hole is drilled where the centre pop was made. All the tips of the rack teeth should be very slightly reduced except the first, so that when the rack hook is raised from the first tooth it will not scrape all the tips of the other teeth when the rack falls.

To find the rack stud centre on the front movement plate a small length of round steel rod should now be driven in the previously drilled hole of the rack centre, whose business end is formed into a miniature centre punch.

Referring to Fig. 23, there is a dot marked S, situated 2 3/16 in. from the bottom of the left-hand movement plate and 2 5/8 in. from the left-hand side of this plate. Position the point of the steel rod in the rack in the vicinity of this spot, and make the gathering pallet gather the rack teeth.

Avoiding wear

The thing to aim at is that the gathering pallet must gather rather more than one tooth at a time, say about one and a half teeth; in other words the rack will recoil a little after each tooth is gathered. This is most important, as if only one tooth is gathered, after a short while any wear that might occur would have the effect of allowing the gathering pallet to gather only the same tooth and make no progress in gathering up the remainder of the teeth.

All this can be observed if the rack is held by the temporary steel centre with its point resting on the movement plate. When satisfied that the correct centre has been found, a slight tap on the steel rod will give the position for the rack stud.

Make the rack stud from mild-steel rod. The question arises as to whether the part on which the rack hub rotates should be turned parallel or tapered as shown in the drawing. Actually, either way is quite satisfactory. If the parallel method is adopted, it is better to drill the hole in the hub first and turn down the spigot of the stud afterwards.

Remove the miniature centre punch from the rack centre and enlarge the hole to fit the spigot of the stud. The depthing of the gathering pallet and the rack teeth can again be tested. Make the rack hub from a piece of brass rod. The rack centre hole will again have to be enlarged to take the spigot of the hub which is now riveted into a countersink on the under side of the rack. Two further brass hubs are next made to a sliding fit over the first hub.

Allow latitude

The bottom hub carries the short rack tail and the upper one the long rack tail. The total distance between the pivot centre of the rack and the pivot centre of the centre wheel of its time train will be the position of the pin in the end of the long rack tail and the pivot centre of the lower minute wheel will be the position of the pin in the end of the shorter rack tail. A little latitude either way will make no difference.

Fig. 36, No. 1. The long rack tail projects either side of the rack centre. The left-hand end carries a small brass weight which is screwed into the circular shaped end of the arm. Its purpose is to cause the rack to fall when the rack hook is raised. The hubs of the two rack tails are not riveted to the central hub, but are clamped to the latter with No. 12 B.A. setscrews.

This allows independent adjustment of the rack tails with their respective snails, which is very convenient. No. 1a is a side view of the rack. The locking pin for the wings of the gathering pallet is 1/8 in. dia.

The short pin of 1/16 in. dia. on the front face of the rack is for raising the musical locking lever, and the longer pin of the same diameter also on the front face of the rack engages with the chime silent lever mechanism situated on the dial plate.

Fig. 36, Nos. 2 and 2a shows the rack hook and its stud. It is cut out from 1/16 in. thick mild-steel plate, and the hook portion is thickened by another piece of the plate riveted to it from the back of the main arm. The right-hand side on the front of the hook is an arc struck from its pivot centre. The left-hand side can be struck from the same centre, although it plays no part in the functioning of the rack hook.

The point of the hook should not completely fill the space between adjacent teeth, which might at first sight be thought desirable. The hook should just lie in the top of the widest space of two teeth tips.

If the hook is shaped as shown in the drawing, this will obtain the approximate pivot centre of the hook, as shown in Fig. 23 at 1/32 in. from the left-hand side of the movement plate, and 2 3/8 in. from the top of the movement plate. The exact position must be obtained by trial in a similar manner as that of the rack pivot centre, bearing in mind that the gathering pallet must gather a good one and a half rack teeth as previously stated.

The locking pin for arresting the wings of the gathering pallet should now be placed. This pin is screwed into the thickness of the rack and it is so placed that when the rack is fully gathered up the tip of the gathering pallet wing will rest on half the diameter of the pin. It is also necessary that when the rack hook is in the space between the first and second teeth of the rack, the tip of the gathering pallet wing must be clear of the pin in the rack.

The hour and quarter snails are better marked out in the clock movement itself. Assuming the rack and the rack hook are ready pivoted on their respective studs and that the blanks for the snails have been fitted to their respective wheels, proceed as follows. Where the pins are to be inserted later in the long and short rack tails, insert, firmly, short lengths of small diameter steel rods with sharp pointed ends.

Taking the hour snail first, before fixing the circular blank to the hour wheel hub divide it into 12 equal segments. The full diameter should be about the same as the hour wheel. Put the rack hook into the fifth tooth space of the rack, then adjust the long rack tail so that the sharp point in its end is just inside the circumference of the blank snail.

Next tighten the clamping screw of the hub and scribe an arc on the first segment of the snail. Move the rack hook into the sixth tooth space of the rack and scribe an arc on the second segment of the snail. This should be continued until all the steps of the snail have been scribed.

It is as well before scribing any of the steps, to try the position of that of one o'clock and 12 o'clock (i.e., the 12 o'clock step must not come too close to the hour wheel hub). The steps of the quarter snail should be scribed out in a similar way.

In this case the rack hook is put into the first tooth space for the first quarter, the second tooth space for the half hour and the third tooth space for quarter to the hour. The fourth segment of the quarter snail as previously stated is cut away so that the pin in the short rack tail does not reach the snail.

The snails should now be removed from the wheels and have the steps cut, taking particular care not to encroach inside the scribed lines. If this be carefully done, and the rack tails are correctly adjusted, the racks should perform their duties perfectly. It should be remembered that when the rack is finally gathered up with the gathering pallet resting on the rack pin, the pin in both rack tails must be clear of the highest steps in the snails.

The proper or final pins for the rack tails should now be made. They are 3/32 in. dia. and are screwed into the thickness of the tails. The tails themselves are made from 1/32 in. brass. The shorter tail falls in the space between the lower minute wheel and the quarter snail, the pin being on the front face of the tail.

The long rack tail falls in front of the hour snail, the pin being in the back face of the rail. It is usual to bevel off the side of the step between one and 12 o'clock of the hour snail, in case failure of the chiming and striking should occur, which would cause the pins in the rack tail to be locked by the long step in the snail if it is not bevelled off.

The lifter, Fig. 36, Nos. 3, 3a and 3b, is cut from 1/16 in. mild steel and the lower area from 1/32 in. sheet brass. The pivot centre is shown on Fig. 31 1 in. from the top of the right-hand front movement plate and 5/32 in. from left-hand side of the plate. There is a stop block riveted to the left-hand end of the upper arm, which goes through a slot cut in the right hand of the left front movement plate.

The angle that the stop block has with the pin in the warning lever where it contacts it is important and needs careful consideration so that the lifter drops smartly away from the pin when the lower arm is released by the quarter pins in the minute wheel.

Projecting from the front face of the lifter and to the right of the stop block is a 3/32 in. dia. pin for raising the rack hook. When the lifter is in its normal resting position, this pin should just be clear of the underside of the rack hook. Its hub and stud are made on similar lines to that of the rack and rack hook.

Fig. 36, Nos. 4, 4a and 4b give the details of the change chime lever, which is made of brass. The steel pin comes through a long circular slot cut in the dial plate. The upper arm is bevelled so that it can pump the rounded end of the chime pivot arbor for changing the tune of the chimes.

The hub of this lever should work quite stiffly on the stud and there is a washer distance piece with a diametrical groove for taking the cross pin which goes through a hole in the stud. The position for the stud is shown in Fig. 23, 7/32 in. from the side of the left-hand front movement plate and 3 9/16 in. from the bottom of the plate.

Fig. 36, Nos. 5, 5a and 5b, shows the details of the chime silent lever. In No. 5 the lower arm is pointing to the right. This, however, when viewing the lever from the front, should point to the left as indicated by the hatched lines.

It is made from brass and cross-pinned to its stud. A pin fixed to the mechanism attached to the back of the dial plate enters the slot in the upper arm of the lever. The stud centre is shown in Fig. 23, 9/16 in. from the left-hand side of the centre front movement plate and 1/8 in. from the top of the plate.

CHAPTER ELEVEN

The levers, weights and pulleys

The levers, weights and pulleys are the subject of this chapter.

Fig. 35, Nos. 2, 2a and 2b. The arms are out from 1/32 in. thick steel. A stop block is fixed at the right-hand end of the horizontal arm and goes through a slot cut in the right-hand front movement plate for arresting a pin in the musical warning wheel.

Its stud centre is seen in Fig. 23, 1 5/16 in. from the left-hand side of the left-hand left-hand front movement plate and 11/16 in. from the top of the same plate.

When at rest, the pin in the back of the rack keeps the stop block in the up position, but when the rack falls away from the left-hand side of the lower arm of the lever, the stop block will drop slightly in the slot and will be in a position to arrest the pin in the warning wheel.

All these levers are retained on their respective studs by small cross pins put in the studs. There must be the minimum amount of end play of the hubs of the levers on the studs.

Musical locking lever No. 1 is shown in Fig. 35, Nos. 3, 3a and 3b. The stud centre is 1/4 in. from the left-hand side of the left-hand front movement plate and 1 1/4 in. from the top of the same plate. The long horizontal arm is cut from 1/32 in. steel plate but the lower arm is cut from quite thin brass plate, say about 1/64 in.

The lower arm has to be springy, for when the rack falls at the hour the pin in its front face will push aside the brass arm and arrive at the under side of the arm. To facilitate this the end of the pin is bevelled off and well polished. There will be no difficulty in obtaining this. The pin in the right-hand end of the upper arm is 3/32 in. dia.

In constructing these levers the arms are generally fitted to the base of the brass hubs and riveted tight but the arms fitting the upper end of the hubs should be partially riveted so that they can move for adjustment. When satisfied the adjustment is correct they should be riveted quite tight.

Musical locking lever No. 2 is shown in Fig. 35, Nos. 4, 4a and 4b. This lever is cut from 1/32 in. steel plate. It is fitted to the end of an arbor that goes between the movement plates. The position for the pivot centre of the arbor is seen in Fig. 31 and marked A, being 15/32 in. from the top of the right-hand front movement plate and 1 1/2 in. from the right-hand side of this plate.

This lever will need a circular recess cut in its bottom edge to gree the hub of the lifter. The arbor is plain sailing and is made from mild-steel rod. MLL 2 is secured to the front pivot of the arbor with a cross pin put through the hub and pivot.

Musical locking lever No. 3 is shown in Fig. 35, Nos. 5 and 5a. The right-hand end of this item is clamped by a setscrew to the pivot of the other end of the arbor.

This pivot projects from the back movement plate. The lever is cut from 1/32 in. steel plate. Note that there is a 3/32 in. dia. pin in its free end for raising the musical locking lever No. 4, shown in Fig. 37, Nos. 1, 1a and 1b.

The change tune lever for the musical barrel, Fig. 35, Nos. 6, 6a and 6b, is made from brass plate and as in the case of the change chime lever it should work stiffly when the distance washer is cross pinned on its stud.

It will be noted that there are three steps on the arc-shaped portion of the lever. It is not necessary to have a fourth step, for when the arc is clear of the end of the pivot of the musical barrel arbor the spring will still be able to pump the arbor sufficiently for the change to the next tune.

Fig. 32a shows the back movement plate mechanism in its relative position on the back plate. Fig. 37, Nos. 1, 1a and 1b, gives details of the musical locking lever No. 4. The pivot centre is 2 in. from the top of the back movement plate and 1 7/8 in. from the right-hand side of the same plate. The lever is cut from 3/64 in. steel plate and the blade at the extreme left-hand end is silver soldered at right angles to the main arm.

The blade that passes through a slot cut in the back movement plate is riveted and silver soldered in position on the main arm. It is as well to cut this blade or stop block to shape after it has been attached to the arm, filing it a little at a time to meet the local requirements.

Fig. 37, Nos. 2, 2a, 3, 4, 5 and 5a, gives the details of the chiming and striking locking lever and its arbor. It is best to begin with the arbor No. 3. This is turned up from a 5 3/8 in. length of mild-steel rod about 9/32 in. dia. The two pivots are

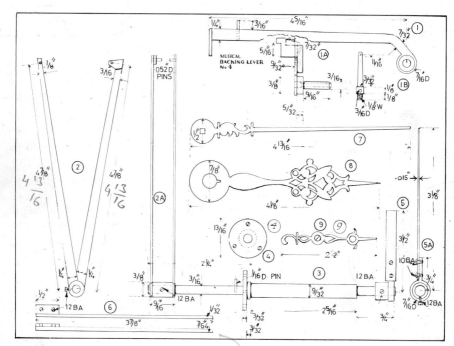

Fig. 37 Details of hands and various levers

turned to a diameter of 3/16 in., the front pivot being 3/4 in. long and the back pivot 2 1/4 in. long.

The back pivot has a separate inserted bearing (No. 4) which is fitted to the back movement plate with three 8 B.A. screws. This separate bearing facilitates the assembly of the arbor between the plates, which can be done after the frame is screwed together.

Nos. 2 and 2a are next made. A brass hub is turned and bored a sliding fit on the back pivot of the arbor. Next the two arms are cut from 3/64 in. steel plate. Before they are cut the two holes that fit the spigots turned on the ends of the hub should be drilled and reamed to size.

The tip of the arm that locks the striking barrel is thickened with a piece of steel riveted to it. One of the arms should be riveted tight on the hub straightaway but the other arm should be partially riveted until adjustments have been made.

When the pin in the upper end of the left-hand arm is resting in one of the slots of the striking barrel the pin in the upper end of the other arm should be just clear of the circumference of the disc attached to the end of the chime barrel, and when the pin in the upper end of the right-hand arm is in the notch of the disc attached to the chime barrel the other arm must be clear of the circumference of the disc attached to the striking barrel.

The hub is clamped to the pivot arbor with a 12 B.A. screw. There is a steel pin fitted to the back pivot of the arbor at a short distance from where the pivot emerges from the back bearing. The pivot is drilled and tapped to take this pin. Next, No. 6, a long thin spring is made and screwed to the back movement plate.

This spring is shown in position in Fig. 32a. Its purpose is to return the pin in the left-hand upper arm into one of the five slots of the striking barrel after the hours have been struck. It can be made from either steel or brass and it is screwed to the back movement plate with two 10 B.A. screws.

Brass spring

Next, the thin long spring (Fig. 37, Nos. 5 and 5a) attached to the front pivot arbor of No. 3 is made from brass shim 1/64 in. thick and is attached by two 10 B.A. screws to the lug formed on the hub which is clamped to the pivot arbor by a 12 B.A. screw (see Fig. 34).

With this clamping method any adjustment can be done to a nicety. The length of spring is such that after the chiming and striking of the hour has occurred it will be released by the pin in the lower minute wheel a few minutes past the hour and after the musical train has completed the playing of the tune.

Fig. 37, Nos. 7, 8 and 9, represents the hands of the clock. The minute hand is cut from 1/16 in. mild-steel plate. Before any cutting is done the square hole that fits the square on the end of the minute wheel tube should be formed by drilling and shaping with a triangular needle file.

This applies to any holes that need drilling in connection with the design of the hands. If this be deferred until the hands have been cut out it will simply wreck them. First, cut out the design in the spade part of the hand; afterwards fine file it up.

Now cut the outline of the side of the hand and fine finish it. And lastly cut the outline of the other side of the hand. To fine finish this last side the hand is clamped in a small machine vice. It is by no means difficult to accomplish.

No. 8. The hour hand is cut from 1/64 in. steel plate and the same remarks as above apply to this hand. It is held to the hour hub by a 12 B.A. cheesehead screw passing through a slot filed from the side of the hole in the hand.

No. 9. The second hand. The same remarks as above. It is screwed to one end of a brass tube approximately 3/32 in. outside the diameter by a 10 B.A. screw with a dome-shaped head. The other end of the tube is cut diametrically through with a fine saw so that it will be a friction fit to the front pivot of the seconds wheel arbor.

All the hands will require polishing on their front faces with fine emery sticks and then carefully blueing by holding them over a small flame from the bunsen burner. A rub with Three-in-One oil will prevent any rust occurring later.

Fig. 38, Nos. 5 and 5a gives the details of the three weight pulleys. The shackles are cut from 1/2 in. square brass rod. A slot is cut to accommodate the pulley wheel. There should be a minimum of play between the sides of the shackle and the sides of the pulley wheel.

The latter runs on a 3/16 in. dia. steel rod, one end of which is threaded 2 B.A. and screwed into one of the sides of the shackles. The hook is shaped from a piece

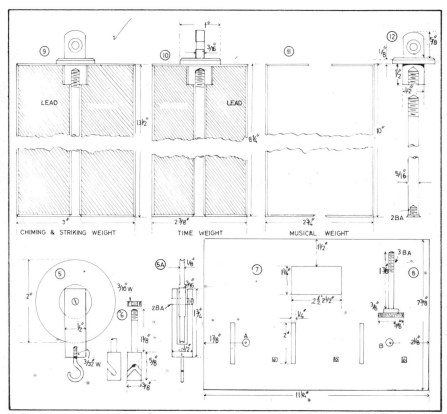

Fig. 38 Details of weights, pulleys, line retaining hooks and movement board

92

of 3/32 in. dia. mild-steel rod and its fixing end is threaded 3/32 in. Whitworth and screwed into the base of the shackle.

Fig. 38, No. 6. Two views of the line retaining hooks for retaining the free ends of the driving lines. These are positioned on the under side of the movement board (No. 7), the spigot passing through the thickness of the board and being held by a nut from the upper side. Three of these will be required.

Fig. 38, No. 7, gives the details of the movement board on which the movement rests. It is made from mahogany about 3/4 in. thick. Three slots are cut through the board for the passage of the driving lines. A larger hole towards the back of the board is cut for the pendulum rod to pass through.

Fig. 38, No. 8, is one of the two set-screws required to hold the movement to the board. They are put in from the under side of the board and are screwed into the central bosses of the two outer bottom pillars of the frame. A and B show their approximate respective positions on the board but their exact location will be obtained with the movement placed on the board.

Nos. 9, 10, 11 and 12, Fig. 38, are the three weight cases. The thickness of the wall of the tube is 1/16 in. A small internal step is turned on the ends of each tube, or a step can be turned on the circumference of the brass discs. The latter is easier to do.

The cases are filled with lead in exactly the same way as that of the pendulum bob. They should not be completely filled as in the drawing, but space should be left so that extra metal can be added for adjustment.

The head of the countersunk screw holds the bottom disc to the base of the tube. The rod passes through a hole in the lead casting. The upper end of the rod is threaded to take the cap whose flange binds and locates the top disc to the upper end of the tube. A cross hole is drilled in the lug above the cap. This hole is chamfered each side to accommodate the hook of the shackle.

The finishing of the weight cases is carried out in the lathe. They are merely emery papered while revolving and given a coat of clear lacquer. Never polish the cases with metal polish; it only enhances defects.

Fig. 39 shows the details of the dial and its fitments. The main dial plate is 1/16 in. brass 10 in. x 10 in. with an extension at the top forming an arch. The distance from the bottom of the plate to the top of the arch is 14 in. The dial plate is connected to the front plates of the movement by four brass pillars. All the details are seen in No. 2.

The 8 B.A. screw in the base of the pillar is cut to the thickness of the dial plate. With this method the base of the pillar will screw right home. The four screwed holes in the dial plate are used for marking the front movement plates for drilling the holes to receive the upper ends of the dial pillars. Care must be taken that these holes do not foul any of the mechanism on the front movement plates.

As soon as the dial plate has been fitted to the movement the three winding holes and the holes for the pivots of the second and minute wheels can be drilled. It is expedient to drill small holes at first, but should these not be quite concentric they can be drawn true with a small file and then the rest of the drilling completed.

In the case of the seconds dial a hole is cut out of the dial plate 2 3/4 in. dia., the seconds dial itself being made separately and screwed to the dial plate from be-

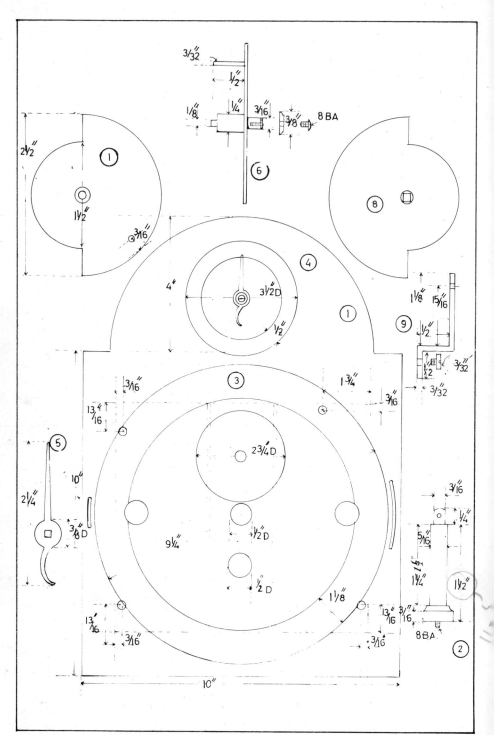

Fig. 39 Details of dial and chimes silent mechanism

94

hind with three 12 B.A. screws. The ends of the screws are cut off flush with the front surface of the dial plate.

Nos. 3 and 4. The chapter ring and chime silent ring. These are superimposed on the dial plate. Small screws are put in from the back of the dial plate to hold them in position. No. 5 is the chime silent hand which is cut from 1/32 in. steel plate. It is polished and blued. Nos. 6, 7, 8 and 9 are the details of the chime silent mechanism.

Chime and silent

The arbor is made from a piece of 1/4 in. round mild-steel rod. The double half circular plate is cut from 1/16 in. brass plate which is riveted to the shoulder of the arbor. The back pivot of the arbor rotates in a hole situated at the upper arm of the cock (No. 9) which is screwed and steady-pinned to the back of the dial plate.

The front pivot of the arbor fits the hole drilled concentric with the chime silent ring. A small square is filed on the pivot to take the chime silent hand. The end of the pivot is tapped to take an 8 B.A. mushroom-headed steel screw. Between the head of the screw and the hand is a brass distance washer whose front surface should be dome shaped and well polished.

A 3/16 in. dia. pin is screwed to the half circular plate. The free end of this pin enters the slotted arm of the chime silent lever working on the stud on the front movement plate.

It is so arranged that when the hand points at chime position the lower arm of the lever will be clear of the pin in the rack, but when the hand is at the silent position the lower arm of the lever will be in contact with the pin in the rack and prevent the latter from falling when the rack hook is lifted.

The two circular slots on each side of the dial plate are for the steel pins attached to the change chime lever and change tune lever respectively to pass through.

A point that has not yet been mentioned is that the retaining collet is screwed to the front pivot of the centre wheel arbor and is not just a push-on fit with a cross pin, which is the more usual method.

CHAPTER TWELVE

The chimes

There remains the pinning of the chime and musical barrel and we begin by plotting the chiming barrel. Trim up a piece of fine note paper to fit the length of the barrel and to fit round the circumference of the barrel, so that the edges of the paper just butt together.

Lay the paper flat and divide the paper into 60 equal parts where it went round the barrel, counting as one division where the edges of the paper met. These lines must be very carefully and evenly set out. Return the paper to the barrel again. (It can be fastened temporarily to the barrel with two rubber bands.)

See that the barrel is pumped by the spring on the cock to the right, that is to say, the shoulder of the front pivot should be in contact with the front movement plate. Mark on the paper the centre of each of the eight hammer tails. The paper is now removed from the barrel and lines are drawn from end to end of the paper which will now show the positions of the hammer tails.

Carefully flatten the paper, and we are ready to plot out the positions for the pins. There will be required five separate peals of eight notes each to be pinned on the barrel, plus five equal rest spaces. Five peals of eight notes to each peal equal 40, and five rest spaces of four note units each equal 20, which added to 40 gives 60 divisions, which have just been made.

The highest note in the peal is called No. 1, and is struck on the smallest bell, and the lowest note is called No. 8, and is struck on the largest bell. No. 1 bell and No. 1 hammer are situated at the right-hand end of the barrel next to the front movement plate.

Fig. 40 is a sketch of the chart for placing round the barrel. The order of the notes in each peal is as follows, starting from the right-hand end of the barrel:

Canterbury Chimes

```
1. – 8 7 6 5 4 3 2 1
2. – 8 6 4 2 7 5 3 1
3. – 8 7 6 5 1 2 3 4
4. – 8 2 7 5 6 3 4 1
5. – 8 1 2 7 3 5 6 4
```

At the first quarter No. 1 peal is chimed, at the second quarter Nos. 2 and 3 peals are chimed, at the third quarter Nos. 4 and 5 peals, followed by No. 1 peal, at the hour Nos. 2, 3, 4 and 5 peals are chimed. Thus it will be seen that the chime barrel makes two rotations per hour.

The St Michael's Chimes

```
1. – 8 7 6 5 4 3 2 1
2. – 8 3 4 2 5 6 7 1
3. – 8 1 2 7 3 6 5 4
4. – 8 3 4 7 5 6 1 2
5. – 8 3 7 5 1 6 2 4
```

To obtain the position of the pins in the barrel for the St. Michael's chimes, with the paper still on the barrel, the change chime lever is now used to pump the barrel arbor towards the back movement plate, and the centres of the eight hammer tails are again marked on the paper.

Referring to Fig. 40 again, it should be noted that the Canterbury chimes have been plotted with solid black dots, and those of St. Michael's with open ring dots. After the pinning of the chime tunes has been done, the paper is returned to the barrel and carefully stuck to it with Bostik cement. An adhesive of a gluey nature is not suitable.

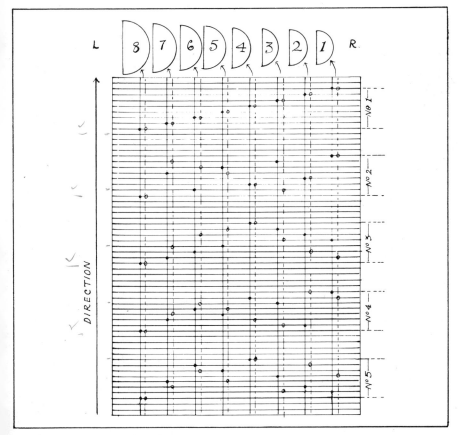

Fig. 40 Chart for plotting chimes

With a miniature centre punch centre pop each dot. Accuracy is the secret of success with this operation. When all dots have been centre popped, strip off the paper chart and drill the holes for the pins. The diameter of the pins is about 0.025 in., and domestic pins known as quills are excellent for the purpose.

The pins must be a tight fit in the holes and a test should be made before drilling the barrel. Each hole can be slightly tapered with a broach if desired. After drilling all holes, insert the pins one at a time and gently tap into position. Now shorten the pins considerably, but leave enough for driving them home. During the hammering process, the barrel must be held in the hand.

Reduce the height of the pins of the first peal to roughly their correct length and return the chime barrel to the movement frame and try the action of the pins with the hammers. When the last pin of No. 1 peal has lifted and disposed of No. 8 hammer, the next on-coming pin of No. 2 peal should be clear (in this case) of No. 1 hammer. The pins in No. 1 peal must be shortened until this is obtained.

Strictly speaking, after a completion of a peal with the gathering pallet locked by the rack pin, the tails of the hammers should be midway in one of the rest positions of the chime barrel. But if this is carried out, the pins in the barrel may give a rather poor lift to the hammer tails with a consequent loss of sound from the bells.

When the length of the pins has been decided, a small jig should be made from a scrap of silver steel. File the thickness of the silver steel to match the height of the pins, followed by drilling a small hole through the steel and then harden the jig. All that it is necessary to do is to slip the jig over each pin in turn, then cut the pins to final length, leaving just a trifle for filing down with the jig in position.

Finally, the ends of the pins should be rounded off with a simple tool made for the purpose. Take a piece of, say, 3/16 in. dia. silver steel, face one end off true, then file a V-notch diametrically across the end, followed by another V-notch filed at right angles to the first notch. Harden the steel and leave it dead hard.

To use the tool, place it over the end of pin and twirl it round a few times. This will have the effect of rounding the end of the pin and burnishing it at the same time. Before inserting any pins in the barrel the latter should be well polished. This will be the last opportunity as it cannot be done after the pins have been inserted.

Pinning the musical barrel is carried out on very similar lines to the chime barrel. The distance round the circumference of the barrel and the length of the barrel should be obtained the same way with a piece of thin note paper. Before choosing the tunes, the following points should be considered.

If two notes of the same pitch follow one another it is preferable to have two hammers to each bell; otherwise the on-coming pin may pick up the hammer tail before it has been discharged by the first pin. It is better to have a tune in which the same notes do not immediately follow each other. An examination of the chart of the tunes of the chimes will explain what is meant.

With a set of 10 bells there is quite a choice of tunes, but this range will not cover all tunes. Assuming the four tunes have been chosen, select the longest tune and count up the number of notes it contains, counting a crotchet as one note unit, a semibreve as two note units, and a breve as four note units.

Supposing the number of note units amounts to 200, it will be necessary to divide the circumference of the barrel into this number of units, but a few extra will be required for the rest period on the finish of the tune. Ten units would be enough, so the barrel circumference would then be divided into 210 divisions. It does not signify if the other three tunes are of shorter duration.

Getting divisions accurate

To get the divisions accurate, I joined up several pages of ruled writing paper and then reduced it by photography so that the required number of lines or divisions would go round the barrel. The photographic print was carefully stuck to the barrel and the centres of the 10 hammer tails were marked with the barrel arbor pumped to the front movement plate.

The change tune lever was moved to the next step, pumping the arbor towards the back movement plate, and again the hammer tail centres were marked on the print. Thus all four hammer positions were marked out this way.

The print was detached from the barrel and lines were drawn indicating the hammer positions for each tune. If different coloured inks are used for each set of hammer lines, it will simplify the plotting out of the positions for the pins.

To do the plotting, put a dot on the appropriate hammer line, and if the note is a crotchet put the next dot on the following division under its appropriate hammer line, but should the first note be a semibreve miss one division and put it on the next division, and so on. It is helpful if a friend calls out the note while one does the plotting.

The chart when fully plotted is stuck to the barrel with Bostik cement and all the dots centre popped on to the barrel. The rest of the work is the same as that of the chime barrel.

A few hints on the general assembling of the movement may prove useful. The wheels of the time train should first be put into position on the back movement plate. First the centre wheel, then the great wheel and barrel, then third wheel and escape wheel, then position the front centre movement plate and put the screws into the pillars.

Now assemble the musical train. The first item is the stud for the maintaining click, see that this engages properly with maintaining ratchet. Screw in position the bottom bracket of the vertical fly and position the great wheel and arbor, then the second wheel, cam wheel, warning wheel, followed by the two idler wheels, and finally the arbor of the musical locking lever No. 2. The front movement plate can now be put on and screwed to the pillars.

To assemble the chime train the stud to the musical locking lever No. 4 should be screwed to the back movement plate. It must be arranged that when the lever is in its normal position the long step of the cam on the cam wheel should be against the stop block of the lever, and at the same time the pin in the warning wheel should have about half a revolution of run to the stop block of the musical warning lever.

Assemble the chime train, great wheel and barrel first, followed by second wheel, pallet wheel, warning wheel and the idler. The relative position of the pallet and warning wheels is important. To get these right the rack and rack hook must be temporarily assembled.

When the gathering pallet wing is locked by the pin in the rack, the pin in the warning wheel must have a run of about a quarter of a turn of the wheel to the stop block of the lifter. The front plate must be lifted for adjusting these two wheels.

The rest of the parts should now be assembled, and attention given to the notch in the disc on the end of the chime barrel. Its correct position is found by making the chime barrel rotate and perform the four last peals as used at the hour.

As soon as the last hammer has been released by the pin in the barrel the disc on the latter should be marked and the notch filled for the pin in the locking arm to fall into. With the chime barrel locked, the disc with five slots attached to the striking barrel can now be adjusted so that the locking pin in the arm will fall centrally into the notches.

When the striking barrel is locked the hour hammer tail must be between two adjacent lifting pins in the disc attached to the striking barrel. This disc, it will be remembered, is made adjustable for this purpose. It should be stated that in doing these adjustments, the wheel work of the train should be kept in the forward position, this is important so that all backlash in the train is taken up.

Trying it out

With all the levers assembled, the chiming and striking abilities of the clock can now be tried out. To get the adjustment just right, as between the chiming and striking barrels, the screw in the fixed arm between the contrate wheels is slightly loosened and the arm moved round the arbor a trifle. A minute amount of movement will make an enormous difference, so care is needed here.

The musical barrel adjustment is quite simple. With the cam wheel locked the hook on the end of the locking lever should be in the centre of the notch of the locking plate. This is easy to obtain as the locking plate is clamped by the setsrew to the extended pivot of the second wheel arbor. The tails of the hammers of the musical barrel should be about midway over the rest period of the musical barrel.

This adjustment can be done with the musical barrel in position by loosening the clamping screw in the set collar in the right-hand end of the barrel and turning the barrel round independently to its gear.

This concludes the construction of the clock. Next follows instructions for making a traditional period case in which to house it.

CHAPTER THIRTEEN

The case

It is not a particularly difficult job to make a case of this kind provided attention is given to small details. The first thing to decide is the wood to be used. Burr walnut veneered on oak or mahogany veneered on oak were the principal woods used by the old makers of clock cases. I chose mahogany.

Rather than use new wood for veneering, it is worth while trying to acquire a piece of Victorian or Edwardian furniture, such as a sideboard, wardrobe or table. The wood—which should be 3/4 in. or 7/8 in. thick—is ideal for a traditional style clock case. The item should be carefully taken apart and any mouldings prized off with a chisel and retained for possible use later.

It may not be necessary to veneer the case all over. The sides can be left plain. What is known as a veneering iron is shown in Fig. 41. The drawing is self-explanatory. The stock and handle are made of hardwood, the blade of brass, well rounded off on the working edge.

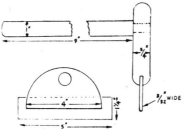

Fig. 41 A veneering iron

A small tool, say with a 1 in. blade, will be found useful for getting into corners. Another essential is a small block plate, the sole of which should be 3 1/2 in. long. Such a plate is most useful for trimming the edges of the veneer, before and after it has been laid. No other special tools seem to be necessary.

A general view of the front of the case with most of the important dimensions marked is shown in Figs. 42 and 43. If a larger case can be accommodated, I would suggest adding a couple of inches to the length of the trunk and long door. My clock goes for 7 1/2 days between windings, which is an ample margin if the clock is wound up about the same time each week.

The first part to make is the front frame of the trunk in which the long door will be fitted later. How it is made up is shown in Fig. 44. The wood should be about 5/8 in. or 3/4 in. thick. The top and bottom members are first sawn out and carefully planed true on all edges, ready for the butt joints with the long members. It is most important that the butting surfaces be finished to an exact right angle with the other surfaces.

Now assemble the frame and glue together. To do this the frame must be laid on a really flat surface. Place paper under the joints so that the frame does not stick to the surface it is laid on. If it is placed on a wood bench, nails can be driven into the bench to clamp the joints together, but if the joints are good, I think this is unnecessary.

A few words on the preparation of glue may be useful. It will be found that ordinary Scotch glue is best. To prepare it, break the cake of glue into small pieces with the hammer, place in the inner pot and cover with cold water and leave it for several hours, or better still overnight.

Heat the water in the outer pot to boiling point remove it and place the inner pot in position. As soon as the glue begins to melt, stir with the brush until it reaches an even texture. It is then ready for use. It should run together when spread on wood without lumps or streaks being present.

Glue should never be boiled and it will be found better to make it up in small quantities for continuous reheating has the effect of taking away its sticking qualities.

The joint should be left for about 12 hours for the glue to harden. The steel screws and nails are then inserted as shown in the drawing. A point worth mentioning here, is that mahogany, be it old or new, has the effect of rusting steel very quickly. For this reason screws that may have to be withdrawn should always be made of brass. The frame can now be generally tidied up.

Having done this, prepare the wood for the back of the trunk as in Fig. 45. The total width of the back is the same as that at the front. The bottom edge of the back falls flush with the bottom edge of the front, but the top end is carried on to form the back of the hood opening. It will be found better to leave this extra long here and cut it to size when the hood is being made.

The sides

The next operation is to prepare the boards for the two sides. The total length of these is about 41 in., but a little extra should be left at the upper ends for final trimming when fitting the movement and dial to the case. The seat board of the movement will rest on the upper ends of the sides. These are about 9 1/2 in. wide. The front edges are flush with the frame and also with the back board of the trunk. They are all butt joints.

The best type of nails to use are known as thin panel pins. Always sink the nail head with a punch. To assemble the trunk it is better to have help from a friend willing to hold the parts together. Always drill a small hole as a guide for the nail.

Before gluing, lightly nail the parts together for position purposes, then separate them. Glue and nail one side at a time and see that the trunk comes out as a rectangle and not a rhomboid—which is quite easy to do unless care is taken. When the glue is set the trunk can be trimmed up where necessary.

Before proceeding with the other parts of the case it would be as well to veneer the front of the frame, and also the sides if this is desired.

Plain veneer is easy to lay (and would do quite well for the sides), but I suggest figured veneer should be used on the frame and front of the case.

To prepare the surface for veneering plane it level and then use a toothing plane.

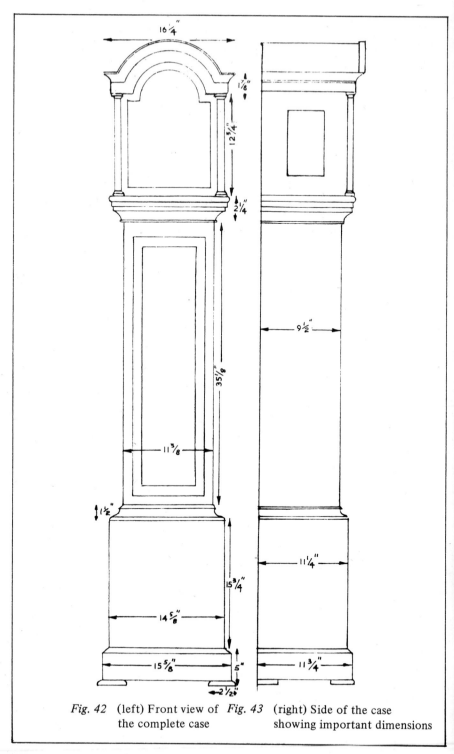

Fig. 42 (left) Front view of *Fig. 43* (right) Side of the case
the complete case   showing important dimensions

This will make a key for the glue, but I have found that a hacksaw blade scraped over the surface with some pressure produces the same result. Cut the veneer into suitable pieces for gluing to the frame. The camouflaged joint should be made as shown in Fig. 44.

A suitable piece of wood—a piece of hardboard does very well—will be needed as a cutting board and also a steel straight-edge and a sharp pen-knife. When shaping the veneer, the knife tends to follow the grain, i.e. it does not really cut the wood but splits it. To avoid this, press lightly with the knife and make it cut gradually through the thickness of the veneer.

To cut across the grain, work from both ends towards the middle, or the veneer will break when the knife arrives at the end of the cut. The veneer should be cut a trifle larger than the surface to be covered, say 1/32 in. or 1/16 in. at the most. The reason is that if there is an excess of protruding veneer the glue, in drying, will pucker it and spoil the joint.

The actual veneering should be done in a temperature of about 65 to 70 deg. If possible warm the veneer and parts to be veneered as well. The fitting edges of the prepared veneer should be lightly planed with the small plane, the veneer being held by hand to the bench and the plane run lightly along it.

Spread newspaper on the bench, melt the glue as previously described and with a medium-size brush quickly spread the glue on the veneer, making sure that all the edges of the veneer have been covered. Place the veneer in position. Dip a second brush in boiling water and run it quickly over the top surface of the veneer, taking care not to let the water touch the glued surface. This will have the effect of softening the veneer considerably. Take the veneering iron and press out the veneer squeegee fashion, starting from the middle and working towards the edges. This will force the excess glue to the edges and cause a suction between the wood and the veneer. The job should be done quickly.

Veneering the frame

To veneer the frame, do the short cross-members first, and then the veneer of the long members can be brought up close to make a fine joint. Press down at the edges firmly, and put aside to dry. Any water remaining on the surface should be wiped off at once. It will take about 12 hours for the glue to dry out properly. Before setting aside, the excess glue can be removed with a stiff brush and boiling water, but care is needed not to unstick the veneer—and always dry off water with a rag.

Much time will be saved later if surplus glue is removed from the edges, so that when they are finally trimmed with the small plane, the blade of the plane is not blunted. If you decide to veneer the sides of the trunk, do this next. In laying a large piece of veneer such as would be required for the sides, proceed as before but only coat 5 in. or 6 in. with glue. Place the veneer in position and treat with hot water and the veneering iron as before.

Lift the veneer back a trifle, coat another section and proceed as before, a section at a time until the whole length of the veneer has been glued. If the veneer is fairly plain and not well-figured, it will present a tolerably smooth surface when dry. On the other hand, if highly-figured veneer has been used, the surface will look

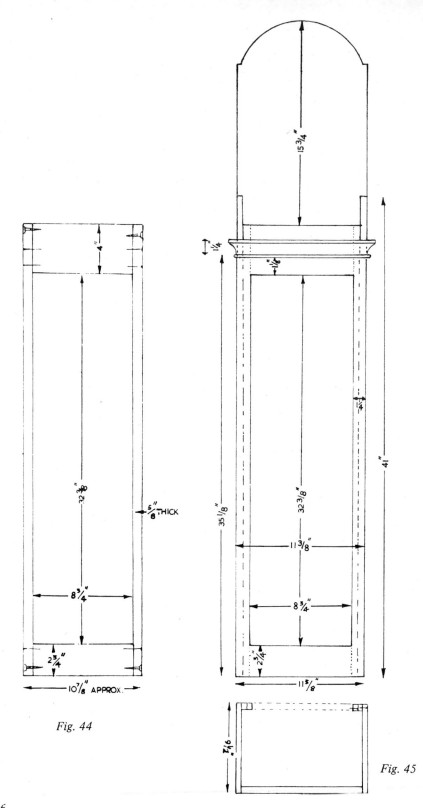

Fig. 44

Fig. 45

somewhat undulating and disappointing.

The next task is to level the veneer down. This can be done by scraping, and I have found a skarsten scraper excellent for the purpose. When dull, the blade can be sharpened easily with a five-grain file. If the veneer is figured, it may be necessary to scrape diagonally rather than with the grain. It all depends on the wood. After this, sandpapering will be needed, but is better left till later on. This finishes the construction of the trunk except for the moulding at the top which will be done later.

The dimensions of the base of the clock case are given in Fig. 46. Usually long cases are made in such a way that the trunk and base are in one piece, but it will be found much easier to construct the base as a separate unit. Before deciding on the dimensions of the base the question of the size and moulding to be used at the junction of the bottom of the trunk with the top of the base must be settled.

The easiest way to do this is to go to the local saw mill and get some quarter-hollow deal moulding such as is used in the building trade. Several sizes are made from about 3/4 in. upwards. A suitable size to use is 1 1/4 in.

The first requirement is a building frame. Fig. 7 shows what is wanted. The width of the horizontal surfaces of this frame must be of such a size as to equal that of the base of the moulding, plus the thickness of the sides and front of the base. There is also the small quarter-round moulding (about 1/4 in.) to be taken into account.

Precise dimension for the building frame cannot easily be given as so much depends on the thickness of the wood used for the sides and the front of the base, mentioned earlier. The building frame can be mitred as shown, or just butt jointed. It should, in any case, be glued and nailed or screwed together.

The base

Assuming that the building frame is made, the sides of the base are glued and nailed to it as shown on the left of Fig. 47. The upper edges of the side should be flush with the vertical and horizontal surfaces of the frame. The front of the base is then glued and nailed, both to the frame and to the edge of the sides, as shown in Fig. 46.

No building frame is needed at the bottom of the base. The sides and front will be glued and nailed as in Fig. 46 and 48. The back view of the base is shown in Fig. 49. The back board to the base is flush with the sides, and joined with a plain butt joint. The top edge of the back board should be level with the top edge of the building frame. The bottom edge of the back board to the trunk rests on the top edge of the back board to the base.

If possible the back of the trunk and base should be from the same piece of wood. The thickness and grain of the wood will then match up nicely.

Before making the skirting, the side and front of the base should be veneered. As the front is fairly wide, it is advisable to veener it in two halves. Have the grain to run up and down the length of the base. The two pieces of the veneer need to be carefully matched as one would do in wall-papering and the join must come dead on centre line.

Veneered plinth

To make the plinth, bevel the top edge of a piece of wood about 1/2 in. thick. The joint at the front and sides should be mitred. The plinth is glued and nailed as before and it will, of course, cover the screws used in joining the front of the base to the sides. The plinth will require veneering and the grain should follow that of the base.

Veneer the bevelled edge first, taking particular care with the mitre at the corners. When the glue is hard plane the front edge of the veneer flush with the surface of the plinth. A point worth mentioning is that when using glue, always roughen the surfaces first.

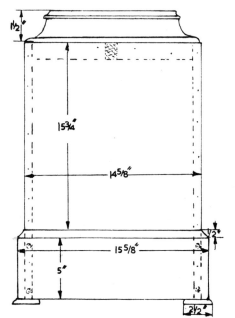

Fig. 46

The feet are made from wood about 3/8 in. thick with a quarter-round chamfer on the front edges. They are mitred at the corners, and glued and screwed into the bottom edges of the plinth. A good idea, in view of the fact that things that stand on four feet usually wobble, is to slightly reduce the thickness of the back feet and then fit a block of wood in the centre of the back of the base, of the same thickness as that of the front feet. This will eliminate wobble—an essential when making a clock case.

Attention can now be given to the fitting of the trunk to the base, Fig. 50. Using a plane, first level up the upper surface of the sides and front, and also the edges at the bottom of the trunk. Position the trunk on the base. The back boards of both the trunk and base should be flush with one another. At the same time there should be an equal space between the sides and front of the trunk and the outer edges of the sides and front of the base. This space will be occupied by the quarter-hollow moulding.

Prepare the mouldings, which should be cut roughly to required lengths. Before

108

cutting the moulding, decide which of its outer surfaces are to be used for the back or bottom. It will be found that the quarter-hollow is not quite perfect in section and if the moulding gets reversed, the corners will not join up properly; so mark one side of teh moulding with a pencil from end to end before doing any cutting.

To veneer the moulding, cut the veneer in suitable sizes as previously stated. When purchasing the quarter-hollow moulding some quarter-round moulding should also be obtained. Only a small quantity will be necessary. This moulding should match the section of the quarter-hollow moulding.

Proceed with the veneering as before, not forgetting to wet with boiling water the surface of the veneer after it has been positioned on the hollow moulding. Quickly press the quarter-round moulding on to the veneer and place in the bench vice and tighten up. Leave for 10 to 15 minutes, remove the counter-die away from the veneered surface and put aside for the glue to dry out.

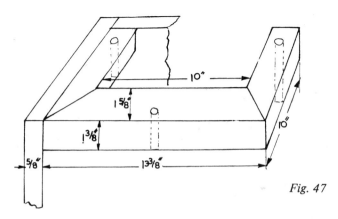

Fig. 47

When set, trim the excess veneer from the edges of the moulding with the small plane, taking care not to encroach on the surface of the moulding. The moulding can then be mitred and fitted into position. The top and side surfaces must be covered by further small mouldings.

The side moulding, which is a quarter-round, can be made quite easily as follows. Get a piece of solid mahogany of the right thickness—say 1/4 in. or 5/16 in. With plane, file and sandpaper, produce a quarter-round section on one edge. Carefully saw through with a fine panel saw, and the moulding is finished. It may need a little dressing up with the plane, perhaps, when it is sawn.

After the large moulding has been fitted and glued it should have a few fine veneer-type nails driven through it into the top of the building frame as indicated in Fig. 49. The small mouldings are put on in the same way, but the use of Croid glue is more convenient to work with. The upper moulding can be produced as a kind of half-round section or made up as two separate mouldings as shown in the drawing.

Fixing trunk to base

To join the trunk to the base get a 12 in. length of screwed steel rod 3/8 in. dia. Drill holes through the top of the building frame as indicated with a suitable drill, assemble the trunk in position, place the drill in holes in the building frame from

109

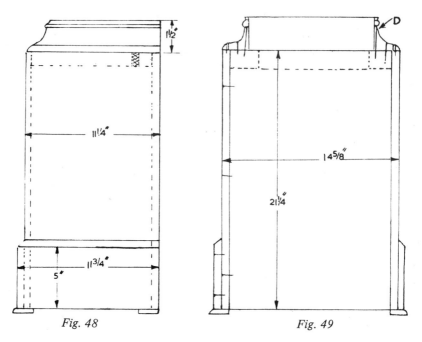

Fig. 48   Fig. 49

below and tap upwards to make a centrepop on the bottom of the trunk. Remove the trunk and drill tapping size holes in the bottom of the trunk, then tap holes and screw the rod in tight. Cut off for length, to allow enough to take thumbscrews which can either be made or purchased. This makes a convenient way for finishing and also for transporting.

Figs. 51 and 52 give details of the long door. The back frame should first be made. Width of wood on face surface about 7/8 in. and thickness about 1/2 in. or more. Plane the pieces until they are nice and smooth. Mitre the corners, and the outside of the frame should be a tight fit in the opening of the frame of the trunk. Glue the corners together and press into the opening of the trunk frame. This will make a splendid clamping arrangement. Take particular care that no winding of the frame has occurred.

Strengthening corners

When the glue is hard, gently knock the frame. The corners should now be strengthened by making two saw-kerfs diagonally across each corner and fitting and gluing two slips of wood. A quicker method is to put in two nails across each corner, taking care to sink the heads of the nails.

The outer frame can now be made. Plane a piece of mahogany about 1/4 in. thick x 1 1/4 in. wide. Mould both edges quarter-round as previously described. It is as well to mark the area to be occupied by the moulding to ensure that the plane does not encroach. Cut and mitre the corner joints. The outer frame is then glued, a piece at a time, on to the back frame. Use a few small veneer pins here and there to clamp it to the back frame. Sink the heads of all veneer pins.

Prepare more veneer. Choose well-figured veneer if possible. Cut it into strips about 7/8 in. wide and with the small plane true the edges on both sides. Mitre the

110

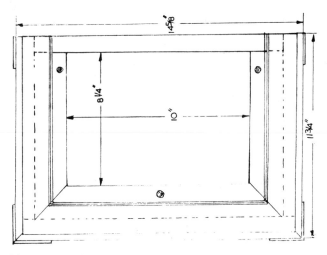

Fig. 50

corners and glue to the frame, taking particular care to get good joints at the mitred corners.

When the glue is hard the door is sandpapered all over. The under-frame should then be made an easy fit to the frame of the trunk opening. In sandpapering take great care not to round off the edges of the veneer which should be clean and sharp. Special hinges for the door and some other fitments will have to be made, but these will be described later.

The hood is really the only awkward part of the case to construct, and it is rather difficult to give precise dimensions of all the details. The first item to be made is the door to the dial. What is important here is that an unnecessarily wide door frame surrounding the dial is to be avoided. If more room is needed inside the hood to accommodate the movement it would be better to fit a larger dial.

Framing the door

It will be found easier to get the proportions of the dial right at the start and build the rest of the hood to fit the dial door. Fig. 53 shows the door with the approximate dimensions. Its final thickness after it has been veneered is about 1/2 in. It can be framed the cabinetmaker's way, that is, morticed and tenoned at the joints. This makes a good job, but great care must be taken not to get any winding.

Another and easier way which is perfectly satisfactory is to get a piece of plywood and mark out the dimensions of the door on both sides. It is important that these dimensions be marked truly opposite each other. With a fretsaw cut out to shape. Do the outside cutting first, plane up to finished dimension. A spokeshave is useful for finishing the curve of the arch.

Cut out the inside, taking particular care not to undercut—which is very easy to do. By glancing occasionally under the wood during the cutting, this undercutting can be avoided. True up the inside edges with the small plane, file and spokeshave, and keep all surfaces square with each other.

The door should be veneered with plain veneer on the inside, followed

111

immediately by the veneering of the outside with figured veneer. Do not forget to veneer all outside edges except that of the arch which had better be done later, when the rest of the hood has been made.

Moulding for door and arch

To produce the quarter-round moulding for the door, proceed as described in making the long door. The moulding should be not more than 1/4 in. wide. To make the moulding for the arch take a piece of mahogany 1/4 in. thick and scribe on the wood the inside and outside diameters of the moulding. With a fine fretsaw, cut out the inner diameter only, and with a file shape the wood to a quarter-round section, being careful not to encroach on to the outer marked diameter. Finish off with sandpaper and then with the fretsaw cut out the outer diameter.

The saw marks can be eliminated by filing. The moulding should be fitted and glued into position. Use Croid glue and pin the mouldings with ordinary domestic pins, the latter being shortened first before driving in. This prevents the pins bending.

The local glass works will cut the glass for the door. An alternative is to use transparent plastic and shape it yourself. Thin fillets of wood are made to hold the glass in position. This is better than using putty, which is, perhaps, more usual. The two pillars as seen in the drawing will be made later.

The front view of the hood (dial door removed) is shown in Fig. 54, with the approximate dimensions. A sketch of the perspective view of the building frame for this is shown in Fig. 55. First, make the two side members. Thickness of wood does

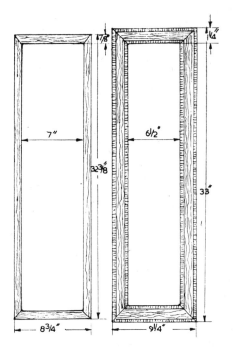

Fig. 51

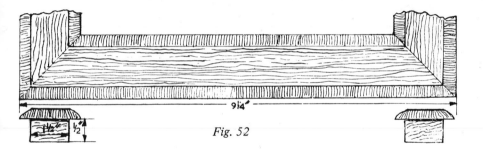

Fig. 52

not matter very much—1/2 in. is suitable, length about 15 in. and width about 9 1/8 in.

The front member of th frame should next be made. It can be framed up or cut out of a piece of plywood to the dimensions shown in Fig. 55. An arched piece is now cut for the back member; note that it butts against the inner surface of the two sides, the width being approximately 1 1/2 in. It is not, at the moment, extended down the side like the front member.

Before assembling the frame, cut out with the fretsaw the windows in the side members. The frame should then be assembled, glued and nailed. All the joints being butt ones, three cross members as strengtheners can be fitted in the roof portion. One is shown in position in the centre. The rest of the hood is attached to the building frame by nailing and gluing.

Fixing the mask

The next thing to do is to cut the mask out of thin plywood (1 mm). This is the same size as the front member of the frame except that the inside edges are extended beyond the inside edges of the front member by 1/8 in. Glue and fix the mask in position, using a few veneer pins to bind it to the wood underneath. The mask should then be covered with plain veneer. Camouflaged mitred or straight joints will be correct. When the glue is set, trim the edges of the veneer and veneer the sides. Camouflaged straight joints are correct here. Glue on the short pieces of veneer first and the veneering should extend to the top of the frame.

The two members for the plinth at the bottom of the hood should be made from solid mahogany. The top member is joined at the outside edges, the edges of the bottom are flat: both are approximately 3/8 in. thick. The upper member protrudes from the sides by 1 1/8 in. and the inner sides butt against the sides of the trunk. They are both mitred at the corners and are a butt fit to the base of the frame. Glue and nail as before.

Movement and dial

Before proceeding with the construction of the hood, the clock movement and dial on its seat board should be tried in position on the trunk. It will be remembered that the sides of the trunk are extended beyond the height of the front frame of the trunk.

The seat board rests on these side pieces or cheeks. With the movement and dial in place, fix the hood in position so that the mask coincides with the dial. Where

113

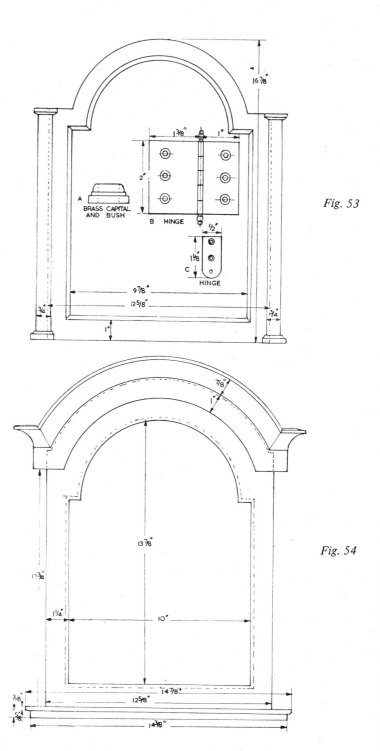

Fig. 53

Fig. 54

the bottom edge of the plinth meets the trunk make a pencil line, which will indicate where the upper surface of the moulding is to be attached to the trunk. The dimensions of the moulding are 1 1/2 in. x 1 1/2 in.

Matters must now be arranged so that when the mask of the hood is aligned with the dial and the hood rests on the upper surface of the moulding of the trunk, the distance from the top edge of the long door to the bottom moulding is approximately 1 3/8 in.

The moulding to the trunk should then be fitted, glued and nailed as before. If a thin nail is used it can be put right through the veneer, the head of the nail nipped off, and a fine nail punch used to sink it below the surface. Details of how to fill the nail hole successfully are given later.

The dotted lines in Fig. 55 give an idea of the arched superstructure of the hood. It is superimposed over the front of the building frame. Its thickness is approximately 1 1/4 in. and it protrudes beyond the top of the dial door by approximately 5/8 in. It can be made from two pieces of wood, if necessary, to get the thickness. Note that the top extends above the building frame by about 1/2 in. and that its width is about 1 7/8 in. Fig. 16a gives further details. The heavy line denotes its width, the upper fine line is where the bottom edge of the hollow quarter moulding will be positioned later.

The arched superstructure should be fixed to the frame with glue, nails and screws. If thought expedient, these can be put into the arch from the back of the frame. Return pieces seen in Fig. 57, should be approximately 1 7/8 in. wide. The hollow quarter moulding will be superimposed on them. The joint of the return pieces with the arched superstructure, can be either mitred or butted.

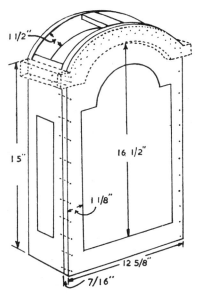

Fig. 55 Building frames of hood

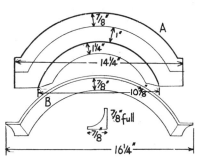

Fig. 56 Details of arch superstructure and moulding of great arch

Veneer both the superstructure and the return pieces. The inside of the arch of the superstructure will also require veneering. At this stage it is convenient to fill in the roof; this is done with a piece of thin plywood. It fits flush with the outer surfaces of the building frame back and front, and is brought down to meet the return pieces each side. Glue and nail in position as before.

Moulding for great arch

The moulding for the great arch should next be dealt with. First, get the deal moulding to be used later for the sides—say 1 in. quarter-hollow. As the average modeller will not have a large enough lathe to produce a similar moulding for the great arch by turning methods, it can be done this way:

Get a piece of deal 1 in. thick, with an even grain and no knots. Draw out the diameters as shown in Fig. 56B. Mark it sufficiently plain to ensure that it won't rub off while being worked on. It is better to make a full half circle of moulding to allow for trimming off, etc.

With a fretsaw, cut carefully along the bottom line of the moulding; then, using a gouge, cut away the wood to form the shape of the hollow moulding, taking particular care not to go beyond the boundaries as marked. In doing this, there is a tendency not to carve away sufficient at the ends of the half circles, so some attention should be paid to this. A template can be made as a guide; finish the carving with light cuts and it will be surprising how true the moulding can be made. Follow on with a scraper filed to shape from mild steel (there is no need to harden the scraper).

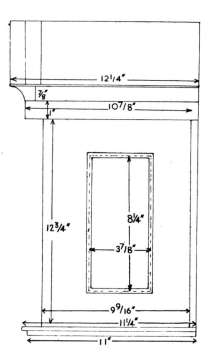

Fig. 57

Making a counter die

The hollow side of the moulding should be covered with newspaper pasted to its surface. On each side of the moulding make paper walls and fasten them to the sides with pins. Mix some plaster-of-Paris and trickle it in on to the moulding. After a short time the plaster will set and can be separated from the moulding. We now have a counter-die. Thoroughly dry this out—continuous gentle heat from the gas oven will do it well. It must be quite dry before being put into use.

Clean off the paper separator from the moulding and slightly roughen its surface with the pointed end of a file or scriber and it is ready for veneering. For convenience, the counter-die can be cut into three or four sections. The veneer will have to be cut to shape to suit the curve of the moulding and will have to be laid in several pieces closely joined; being a curve both ways it cannot be veneered in one piece. Small cramps, such as are used in fretwork, will do the cramping.

After gluing is complete, leave to set for two hours or so before removing the cramps. Trim up the edges of the veneer and clean away all the excess glue. There may be gaps in the jointing of the veneer, but these can be filled up later when the nail holes are done. Next, the return mouldings for the sides will required veneering. The great arch moulding can be cut to size, fitted, glued and pinned in position over the arch superstructure.

Fit the short return moulding at the ends of the great arch moulding. The angle at the joint here is about 55 deg. All mitres at the corners should be carefully finished, but as sometimes happens, a bad one will occur, come what may. To rectify this, shave some scraps of veneer wedge-shape. Fill the gap with glue and push in the veneer wedge; do not wash away the excess glue. Leave it to harden and it will be found that the offending mitre can be trued up with file and knife and a perfect corner will result.

CHAPTER FOURTEEN

The hood and pillars

Attention should now be given to the back of the hood. As left, the sides were held together by the arched-shaped member at the top of the building frame. It will also be remembered that the back board of the trunk was deliberately left full-length for later adjustment to fit the arch piece of the back of the hood. These can now be cut to make an easy fit with each other. In doing this, see that the underside of the arch of the hood will clear the top of the bells, and also the top of the arch to the dial. The hood will eventually make a sliding fit on to the trunk.

Pieces of wood are next cut to fill in the space between the back of the hood and the back of the trunk. These pieces protrude externally and internally beyond the sides of the hood by about 1 in. They are made of wood about 3/8 in. thick and can be veneered on their front surfaces if desired. To make the back of the hood tidy it may be necessary to add a thickness of wood superimposed over the arch member, to bring it level with the side pieces just mentioned.

Fig. 18 represents the plan view of the roof to the hood. C shows the upper edge of the great arch moulding which should be veneered. The top side of the arch superstructure, B, can also be veneered to make it tidy. At A a strip of veneer should be fixed to cover the nail heads. The "flats" or "lands" at E and D should be covered with thin strips of mahogany. These can be fitted on their inner sides to make a neat joint with the curved plywood roof covering. The outer sides of the "lands" should be bevelled off, as indicated in Fig. 57 and 54.

There remain only the pillars and the brass "furniture". The pillars are made from 3/4 in. diameter deal or birch rod; they will require veneering. Cut the veneer to size. It is not necessary that the veneer should make a close joint down the length of the rod, for it will have to be cut away later.

To do this veneering requires an assistant. Have prepared in advance some old rag material, cut into strips. Glue the veneer, lay it on the bench, lay a rod in the middle of the veneer, roll the veneer around the rod and get your assistant to bind on the rag strips puttee fashion (a real sticky job this!). Bind the veneer closely and leave a few hours for the glue to harden. Then gently remove the rags and clean away excess glue.

Cutting the pillars

Cut the pillars to fit between the plinth at the base of the hood and the underside of the arch superstructure. At the joint of the veneer, cut out a right angle section about 3/16 in. sq. Clamp the pillar in the bench vice and do the cutting with a fine tenon saw. The cut can be trued up if necessary with a square-side file.

The left-hand pillar can be glued to the corner of the dial door, but I prefer to

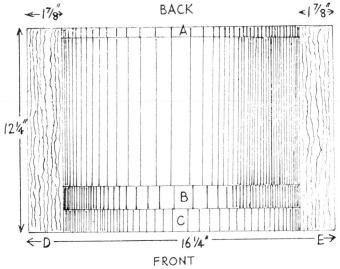

1 7/8"

1 7/8"

12 1/4"

A

B

C

D

16 1/4"

E

FRONT

Fig. 58 Plan of the roof to the hood

attach it by a thin screw put in from the top and bottom of the pillar at an angle of 45 deg. The right-hand pillar is cut out the same way, but instead of being attached to the corner of the door it is attached to the brass capital and base. Three pillars in all will be required—two for the front of the hood, and a quarter-pillar each side of the hood. Small half-round mouldings must be made to finish off the windows in the sides of the hood. These are easily produced with a small plate and file. They should be fixed with Croid glue and pinned.

Five capitals and bases will be required—four for the two front pillars and one cut into quarters for the two back pillars. These are made from 1 1/8 in. square brass rod. Chuck the brass rod in the four-jaw chuck and turn at first a plain cylindrical spigot. The final shaping can be done with a hand graver or form tool.

Bore out to the size of the diameter of pillar, to which it should be a tight fit. In the case of the left-hand capital and base, fine countersunk brass screws put in from the sides will hold them securely to the pillar. The right-hand pillar will not be attached to the corner of the dial door. The capital and base will be a tight fit to the pillar, and the latter are attached to the superstructure and plinth with countersunk brass screws as shown at A, Fig. 53.

Hinges for the dial door are cut out of sheet brass, say 1/16 in. thick, and fitted on the right-hand corner of the dial door. A small brass countersunk screw passes into superstructure and plinth. Note that the capital and base will cover these hinges and will need a sink made in the former to clear the thickness of the hinges.

The outside of the arch on the right-hand side of the dial door near the corner may need easing off a trifle to allow it to pass from under the arch of the superstructure. It is a peculiar action and best observed on sight. All that remains is to fine finish and sandpaper up to a good surface. It is well worth spending some

119

time on this process. I have found garnet paper excellent for finishing—it does not appear to clog so quickly as sandpaper.

Hinges for the long door have yet to be made. These are shown in Fig. 53B. From a length of 1/16 in. thick x 1 3/8 in. wide brass strip, cut out the flat portions of the hinges. Obtain some small thin brass tube about 1/8 in. dia. Cut into four pieces a little longer than the length required for the hinges. Clean the brass tube and one long side of each of the brass pieces with emerypaper. Treat with Easyflo flux, assemble the brass tube and brass pieces together on the soldering block.

A small piece of metal should be placed against the brass tube to prevent it from moving during the soldering. Three small pieces of silver solder, one at each end and one on the centre, should be enough to make a good joint. Heat carefully, directing the heat more on the brass strip rather than on the tube. The solder should now flow like water from end to end.

When soldered, clean and file the ends of the tube flush with the ends of the brass strip. The tube portions will now be marked into five equal sections. Cut through the tube with a fine-bladed fretsaw and also cut away alternate sections of the tube, taking into account that the corresponding sections will remain with the other half of the hinge.

Fitting the hinges

Fit the brass pin which, it will be noted extends beyond the top and bottom of the hinge by about 1/8 in. These ends are threaded and finials are made and screwed on. The hinges can now be fitted to the door and case. They protrude from the face of the door by about 3/8 in. This is necessary to allow the moulding on the right-hand door (side door) to clear the door frame when the former is opened. The wider side of the hinge is fitted to the frame of the case.

To fill the nail holes, get some sealing wax, of suitable shades. Place some of the wax in a small tin and melt over a bunsen burner. By mixing the colours together a suitable shade can be got to match the colour of the wood. It is as well to have the shade a trifle darker than the wood.

When well mixed, pour the wax on a sheet of glass, and before it has hardened, remove and roll into sticks about 3/32 in. dia.—the smaller the better. Take the tang end of a file and heat it. Touch the end of wax so that it melts and drops into the nail hole. Immediately press down the wax with the finger. It will harden at once and can be levelled off with a chisel, followed by sandpaper. It makes a perfect union with the wood, and if the matching has been well done it will be invisible after the french polish has been applied.

Plenty of information is available about how to do french polishing. I would like to stress one point—the filling of the grain with prepared filler before polishing is commenced. Do *not* do this—it will kill the beauty of the wood and leave it patchy in appearance under the polish. After sandpapering, rub linseed oil into the veneer, making sure to go into all the corners and angles. This is most important. Rub off as much of the oil as possible and leave to dry out for a couple of days. The oil has the effect of darkening the wood.

The case is now ready for french polishing which at first may be quite freely applied—either with a brush or rubber. The first few coats will just go into the wood. When it is seen that there is some polish on the surface, rub down with No. 9 garnet paper or steel-wool (I prefer the latter). This will remove the polish from the surface, but the grain will remain partly filled with it. Continue this treatment as before until the grain is quite filled up. It will take many coats and seem a tedious process, but the final results are well worth it. When the grain is quite filled up french polishing proper can be commenced.

CHAPTER FIFTEEN

Finishing the dial

We now come to details for finishing off the dial and in particular how to do the engraving and silvering of the chapter ring and the chime silent ring.

To make the chapter ring, proceed as follows: Mount a circular piece of wood on the faceplate of the lathe (plywood does very well). It should be secured firmly to the faceplate with woodscrews put in through the slots of the faceplate using washers under the screws if necessary. Now turn the circumference of the wood a little larger than that of the chapter ring.

At the centre of the wood disc insert a brass woodscrew, leaving the head of the screw protruding a trifle. Turn down the head of the screw to about 1/8 in. dia., and make a fine centrepop in the end of the spigot. Mark out the circumference of the chapter ring, and cut carefully to size with the fret saw; a centre hole should be drilled in the chapter ring plate so that it is a snug fit to the spigot on the wooden disc.

The chapter ring can now be positioned on the wooden disc and held to it by putting drawing pins through the holes that will be used for attaching the chapter ring to the dial plate. Now turn true the outer circumference of the chapter ring and remove faceplate from the lathe.

The figures should be drawn on the chapter ring, but first the surface of brass should be dulled. A little pumice stone powder and water rubbed on the surface of the metal will do this, or the metal can be given a coat of gamboge and water. This will make it easy to draw on. The illustration shows how the figures should be drawn.

Take particular care that the spaces between the thick strokes of the figures are kept narrow. They should be much narrower than the strokes of the figures to look well.

The Vs of five, six, seven and eight must not be spread, and the same remark applies to the Xs for nine, ten, eleven and twelve. When all is drawn in, go over each figure with a sharp scriber. The chapter ring and faceplate should now be returned to the lathe, and the circular lines should be engraved with a fine pointed tool in the slide rest. I find it better to move the faceplate round by hand. The fine lines at the top and bottom of the figures are also engraved at the same time.

Remove faceplate from the lathe and engrave the fine straight strokes of the figures. This should be done by hand engraving. A small square or lozenge-shaped graver is all that is required—one about 1/8 in. square section does very well. Whet it well on an oil stone. When right the point of the graver should dig into the back of one's thumbnail. It is better to sit on a low seat so that the work is just above eye level.

Fig. 59 Dial, one third full size

This should be done by hand engraving. A small square or lozenge-shaped graver is all that is required—one about 1/8 in. square section does very well. Whet it well on an oil stone. When right the point of the graver should dig into the back of one's thumbnail. It is better to sit on a low seat so that the work is just above eye level.

If the graver is sharpened correctly, practically no pressure is needed to follow the trough of the scribed lines. Cut from both ends of the figures if necessary. Inclining the graver to the left will make a broader but shallower cut, and inclining it to the right will make a deeper but finer cut.

The broad strokes of the figures are treated as follows: drill a small hole through the middle of each broad stroke. Then, using a fine piercing saw, completely cut away the area of the stroke, keeping however, just within the scribed lines. With a fine flat-sided needle file true or justify all the margins cut by the piercing saw. The divisions on both the seconds dial and chapter ring can easily be done by hand engraving. Remove any burrs left by the engraving using s small piece of emery stick. The chapter ring and faceplate are then returned to the lathe, and the inner

123

circumference of the chapter ring should be scribed and parted through. A slight chamfer on this edge will enhance the appearance of the chapter ring.

The chapter ring can then be removed from the faceplate. Some thin paper should be pasted on to the back of the chapter ring, and for convenience it can be replaced on the faceplate. A few drawing pins will hold it in position. The chapter ring is now heated with the bunsen burner, making it sufficiently hot to allow sealing wax to melt and run when contacting the metal.

Fill the engraving and pierced work with the wax, making no attempt to control its flow or position. When the engraving is sufficiently filled with wax, reheat the chapter ring, and with the edge of a piece of fine card (a business card is ideal) scrape away the excess wax. When cool, remove the chapter ring from the faceplate, place it under cold water and scrape away the remaining excess with a small piece of flat pumice stone. Care should be taken to keep the chapter ring well moistened with cold water.

Silvering the chapter ring

The paper on the back of the chapter ring can then be taken from the back of the ring. After drying the chapter ring replace on the faceplate, run the lathe at medium speed and grain the front surface of the ring with emery-paper—say No. 1 fine or coarse No. 0—wrapped around a piece of flat cork. Great care must be taken to ensure that the wax does not soften with the friction, as this would cause smears on the chapter ring. Remove the chapter ring from the faceplate without touching its front surface with the fingers. It is then ready for silvering.

Get a small quantity of nitrate of silver crystals, in half a tumblerful of water. Fill the tumbler with water and add a dessertspoonful of ordinary salt. The silver will fall to the bottom of the tumbler. After a few minutes pour off the water leaving the silver-chloride behind.

Refill the tumbler with water and stir up the silver-chloride to thoroughly wash it. When it has settled again pour off the water. Do this three times to get rid of the acid. Finally the water is poured off, and the silver-chloride mixed with an equal quantity of cream of tartar and salt (proportions do not really matter). Well mix and the paste is ready to be used.

Rub the chapter ring all over with the paste, using either a piece of cotton pad or the fingers. I prefer the fingers. It must be fairly quickly applied with a circular movement. At first it will go black and cloudy, but on continuing the treatment it will eventually turn to a nice white surface of silver. Nothing is gained by applying an excessive amount of paste because this is a chemical action and the brass surface will only absorb a limited quantity of the silver.

When an even surface has been obtained, rinse the ring with warm water and with a small brush, clean out the corners of the engraving and any screw holes. This is very important, as any paste left on the chapter ring causes dark spots to appear. If this happens, it can be removed with cotton-wool dipped in water and cream of tartar. For this reason it is better to leave the lacquering for a week or so.

To lacquer the chapter ring, use clear lacquer known as "Sprayt" made by M. Munster Developments Co., of Fulham, SW. The lacquer should be diluted to about half strength with amyl acetate, and applied quickly but sparingly, or the wax will "cry" and spoil the appearance of the ring.

The letters on the chime/silent ring are marked out in the same way as those on the chapter ring. They are then carefully cut through with a fine piercing saw. To get good results go carefully as the letters are too small to be trued up after cutting with a needle file. The letters are filled with the wax in exactly the same way as the chapter ring.

The brass dial plate is polished and lacquered except where it shows within the chapter ring and chime/silent ring. These portions are grained with emerypaper. The graining should be kept vertical and afterwards silvered, which will contrast well with the circular graining on the rings. The spandrels are better purchased, but can be cast if one has facilities for doing this. The spandrels may be obtained from Rowley, Parkes and Rowley, Briset Street, Clerkenwell Road, EC2. They are attached to the dial plate with a screw inserted from the back of the dial plate.

The fret to the centre of the dial is rather an optional feature. It does, certainly, furnish it well. On the other hand, the hands of the clock show up clearer without it. The fret is cut out of 1/32 in. brass plate with the fret saw, and all edges carefully fine finished with file and emerypaper. The front surface is then polished. The fret can be attached to the dial plate with, say, three 10 BA screws, but I attached mine with three short thin lugs that passed beneath the inner circumference of the chapter ring. These lugs are shown in the drawing shaded, two being at the top of the fret and one in a midway position at the bottom of the fret.

The lettering of the inscription is cut out of thin sheet steel, say about 1/64 in. thick. A fine tooth piercing saw is required for this operation. The pattern of the letters was taken from a magazine, the letters being cut out and stuck to the steel plate with Bostic clear cement. No other form of adhesive seems so suitable. After fretting out the letters, they are touched up here and there with a fine needle file and their face surfaces made smooth and bright on an emery stick. Afterwards they are blued over a bunsen burner. They are then cemented to the fret with a suitable cement. Finally the front fret is given a coat of lacquer.